Space Weapons and the Strategic Defense Initiative

CROCKETT L. GRABBE

IOWA STATE UNIVERSITY PRESS / AMES

Crockett L. Grabbe

Crockett Grabbe, a research scientist in physics at the University of Iowa, is involved in research on wave propagation and instabilities in space and laboratory plasmas.

Manufactured in the United States of America
⊛ This book is printed on acid-free paper.

First edition, 1991

Library of Congress Cataloging-in-Publication Data

Grabbe, Crockett L.
    Space weapons and the strategic defense initiative / Crockett L. Grabbe. — 1st ed.
        p.   cm.
    Includes bibliographical references and index.
    ISBN 0-8138-1277-1 (acid-free paper)
    1. Astronautics, Military—United States.   2. Space warfare.   3. Strategic Defense Initiative.
    I. Title.
    UG1523.G69   1991
    358′.8′0973 — dc20   90-28897

Contents

Epilogue, 143

Appendices

Preface

         Space weapons and the Strategic Defense Initiative have been important topics of discussion and debate in the scientific, engineering, military, and arms control communities and have been a focus of many citizens concerned about the future of security, space development, and the arms race. This book has been written to give an overview of much that has developed since the Strategic Defense Initiative in 1983; what the systems undergoing research and development in this program are; the implications of these systems for arms control; and the prospects, weaknesses, and potential dangers of a strategic defense against nuclear missiles.

    The main body of the book has been written for a general audience interested in the developments, prospects, and implications of space weapons for the United States. The appendices contain more scientific descriptions and analyses of selected topics, as well as reprints of documents and treaties related to strategic defense and space weapons. After an introduction in Chapter 1, Chapters 2–7 give an overview of the systems planned or under development for a strategic defense and their possible shortcomings. Chapters 8–10 examine implications for these systems for the arms race and arms control in general. Chapter 11 reviews the events in Europe associated with the Strategic Defense Initiative, and Chapter 12 examines related issues.

    In much of the discussion in this book the Soviet Union is taken as the "aggressor" against whom the strategic defense would defend. There are two major reasons for this. The Soviet Union is the only other country with a large arsenal of nuclear weapons and long-range ballistic missiles. Furthermore, its nuclear capabilities provided the primary motivation for adopting the Strategic Defense Initiative. However, most of the discussion would apply to any nuclear power, present or future, capable of attacking the United States. (See the epilogue for recent developments.)

    I would like to thank John Pike of the Federation of American Scientists, James Bruce, a counsel for the Senate, and Matthew Bunn of the

Arms Control and Disarmament Agency for helpful discussions on topics in this book. I am also very grateful to Tim Eastman of the University of Maryland for reading a draft of the manuscript and making a number of comments and suggestions and to Kosta Tsipis of the MIT Program in Science and Technology for International Security and Carl Sagan of the University of Cornell for helpful comments on an early draft of the manuscript. Appreciation also goes to John Birkbeck at the University of Iowa for drafting many of the figures and to Douglas Waller of *Newsweek* and Steven Aftergood and Peter Boyer, both of the Federation of American Scientists, for providing useful reports.

Acronyms

ABM	Anti–Ballistic Missile
ALE	Airborne Laser Experiment
ALPS	Accidental-Launch Protection System
ALS	Advanced Launch System
AMRAAM	Advanced Medium-Range Air-to-Air Missile
AOA	Airborne Optical Adjunct
ASAT	Antisatellite
ATBM	Anti-Tactical Ballistic Missile
ATP	Acquisition, Tracking, and Pointing
BEAR	Beam Experiment Aboard Rocket
BM/C³	Battle Management with Command, Control, and Communication
BMD	Ballistic Missile Defense
BSTS	Boost-Phase Surveillance and Tracking System
C³I	Command, Control, Communication, and Intelligence
DARPA	Defense Advanced Research Projects Agency
DEW	Directed-Energy Weapon
DNA	Defense Nuclear Agency
DOD	Department of Defense
DOE	Department of Energy
EDI	European Defense Initiative
EMP	Electromagnetic Pulse
ERIS	Exoatmospheric Reentry Vehicle Interceptor System
FEL	Free-Electron Laser
HEDI	High Endoatmospheric Defense Interceptor
HOE	Homing Overlay Experiment
ICBM	Intercontinental Ballistic Missile
INF	Intermediate Range Nuclear Forces
KEW	Kinetic-Energy Weapon
KKV	Kinetic-Kill Vehicle

LACE	Laser Atmospheric Compensation Experiment
LAMP	Large Advanced Mirror Program
LIDAR	Light Detection and Ranging
LISE	Laser Integrated Space Experiment
MHV	Miniature Homing Vehicle
MIRACL	Mid-Infrared Advanced Chemical Laser
MIRV	Multiple Independently Targetable Reentry Vehicle
MOU	Memorandum of Understanding
MX	Mobile-X (a U.S. counterforce ICBM capable of being shuttled between silos)
NASA	National Aeronautics and Space Administration
RV	Reentry Vehicle
RME	Relay Mirror Experiment
SALT	Strategic Arms Limitation Talks
SATKA	Surveillance, Acquisition, Tracking, and Kill Assessment
SBI	Space-Based Interceptor
SDIO	Strategic Defense Initiative Organization
SIDE	Sensor Integrated Discrimination Experiment
SLBM	Submarine-Launched Ballistic Missile
SS-17, 18, 19	(Specific types of current Soviet ICBMs)
SS-4, 5, 20	(Specific types of Soviet intermediate-range missiles)
SS-12, 21, 22, 23	(Specific types of Soviet medium-range missiles)
SS-24, 25	(Specific types of new Soviet counterforce ICBMs)
SSTS	Space-Based Surveillance and Tracking System
START	Strategic Arms Reduction Talks
TBM	Tactical Ballistic Missile
TDI	Tactical Defense Initiative
THOR	Tiered Hierarchy Overlay Research
TIR	Terminal Imaging Radar
XRL	X-Ray Laser

Space Weapons and the Strategic Defense Initiative

Military Uses of Space

The Beam-Weapon Flap

Headlines appeared on radio, television, and a number of newspapers: "Soviets Develop an Antimissile Particle Beam." They created an outburst of concern across the country. Reports stated that *Aviation Week and Space Technology* revealed important new evidence that the Soviets had made major breakthroughs in the development of particle-beam technology for military use and had working particle-beam weapons. This information was leaked to the magazine in early May 1977 by a general who was the former head of Air Force Intelligence, Maj. Gen. George J. Keegan.

The issue became a cause célèbre among a number of leading spokespersons for a stronger defense. For example, the issue became an almost daily topic of discussion on a late-night radio talk show in the Los Angeles area. It presented a new reason that the United States needed the B-1 bomber and long-range cruise missile since they might be the only devices that could penetrate the new particle-beam weapon invented by the Soviets. By some reports one might believe that the Soviets had moved years ahead of us with this development and that we had better mobilize and start pushing a few weapons to penetrate this shield before it was too late.

The other side of the issue emerged, however, as arms experts examined claims about these new developments. The issue had been debated within the intelligence forces themselves for some time, and the consensus was that intelligence data gathered on the secret installation of the particle-beam weapon near the city of Semipalatinsk in Kazakhstan in the Soviet Union did not support any such conclusion. So General Keegan took the issue to the press.

Physicists experienced in military weaponry pointed out that there were serious questions about the feasibility of such a weapon and even greater questions about its capacity to protect the Soviet Union against intercontinental ballistic missiles. The story was created from bits and pieces of information gathered on Soviet facilities whose purpose was not fully understood, even though there were several other explanations of the data. Furthermore, even if the Soviets had made several independent major breakthroughs that had somehow eluded American researchers on particle beams, they would still be many years away from the deployment of these weapons. Thus the concern was not justified.[1]

The issue soon died after several experts published the difficulties with the speculations of Keegan and the even greater difficulties of developing systems similar to the ones discussed and then being able to make a useful defense out of them. It became clear that there was nothing to the flap. Beam weapons were out of the public's mind. But not for long.

The Strategic Defense Initiative

On March 23, 1983, President Reagan stated in an address to the nation: "What if free people could live secure in the knowledge that their security did not rest upon the threat of US retaliation to deter Soviet attack, that we could intercept and destroy strategic ballistic missiles before they reached our own soil? . . . I call upon the scientific community in our country . . . to turn their great talents now to the cause of mankind and world peace, to give us the means of rendering these nuclear weapons impotent and obsolete." So began the Strategic Defense Initiative (SDI), in which the United States has embarked on a major effort to develop a nuclear defensive capability. (See Appendix 1 for the complete text of the part of that national address on the Strategic Defense Initiative.)

The goal as set out by President Reagan was to build a defense that would protect the population in the United States from nuclear attack, and to do so with perfect or near-perfect confidence. This proposal brought to public light a low-level research program that had been carried on for more than a decade before, and considerably expanded it. Shortly afterward, the president claimed that what he was proposing was research (which was already going on), but the subsequent proposed budget for this research (initially $26 billion for 5 years) indicated a substantial expansion of work on such defenses. This first phase was given the name "research and technology phase," since the more usual (and probably more accurate) term "research and development phase" would imply a violation of the

1972 ABM Treaty. (That treaty and its possible violations are addressed in Chapter 10.)

The goal of a total defense of the land mass of the United States set out by the president was supported by Secretary of Defense Caspar Weinberger. A few days after Reagan's speech he stated on a "Meet the Press" interview that "the defensive systems the president is talking about are not meant to be partial. What we want to try to get is a system which will develop a defense that is thoroughly reliable and total. And I don't see any reason why that can't be done."

However, many in the Defense Department and the Pentagon have never really supported the idea that the purpose of such a defense is to protect populations against missiles and are in general quite skeptical of such a goal. This is despite the fact that in general they have strongly supported the idea of building the defense. As Edward Gerry, former director of the strategic technology office in the Defense Advanced Research Projects Agency, said in 1984 congressional testimony, "[The Fletcher commission committee Gerry headed] recognized from the outset that a completely leakproof defense is certainly impractical if not impossible."[2] The majority of the individuals associated with and supporting this program have admitted that "confident damage denial" cannot be achieved.

Many in the Defense Department have seen the primary utility of a space missile defense to be that of defending missile silos and military installations, as well as adding flexibility to the strategic options available (i.e., to assist the offensive forces). These goals have been the declared purpose by many managers of the program for several years. A 1985 Office of Technology Assessment report on ballistic missile defense stated: "Although some people have interpreted some of President Reagan's statements to mean that he envisions development of a virtually perfect defense of the US population against all types of nuclear attack, pursuit of defenses able to protect the US population and that of its allies in the face of a determined Soviet effort to overcome them does not appear to be a goal of the Strategic Defense Initiative program."[3] The panelists, a majority of whom were associated with the military, recognized that the Soviets can always counter a population defense using several measures or penetration aids to assure that the missiles get through. Similar views have been expressed in Defense Department publications dealing with SDI.

The purpose that many have seen in the space missile defense is one of enhancing deterrence. They have been concerned about the Soviet Union developing a first-strike option with their land-based missiles and see a space defense as a way of countering that potential. (An analysis of the role of an SDI defense in possible first-strike strategies is made in Chapter

8.) On the other hand, the former president and secretary of defense saw an SDI defense as a way of bypassing deterrence by making it unnecessary. These two purposes are contradictory.

The fact that enhancing deterrence had been the proclaimed purpose by several in the Strategic Defense Initiative Organization (SDIO) led President Reagan to declare before the National Space Club in April 1985 that SDI was "not . . . a concept just to enhance deterrence . . . not just an addition to our offensive forces, but research to determine the feasibility of . . . a shield that could prevent nuclear weapons from reaching their targets." The president's science adviser Keyworth clarified this to mean that "protecting weapons represents no change in present policy. It simply strengthens — entrenches — the doctrine of mutual assured destruction. Protecting people, on the other hand, holds out the promise of dramatic change."[4]

Former Secretary of Defense Weinberger addressed a nuclear deterrence panel at Harvard in September 1986 in which he disputed claims that the Reagan administration was reorienting its program to missile-site defense rather than population defense. The basis of these claims was the technical challenges and difficulties that were becoming apparent and the budget cutbacks in the program. However, Weinberger stated, "When the President says that we are aiming at a strategic defense designed to protect people, that is exactly what he means." Professor Albert Carnesale of Harvard University, who served on the panel, stated, "If we really want to defend our society, we have to think about other sources of defense — cruise missiles and bombers, and weapons hidden in bales of marijuana, which we certainly cannot keep out of our cities."[5]

The Reagan administration would clearly have been in a bind if it suggested that the goal was only to assist other military forces and not to make the revolutionary step of shielding the country from nuclear attack, since a large part of the attractiveness of the system would then wear off. Given the huge cost that may be involved in building the defense, the expected payoff would have to be highly rewarding to justify the research and development program. So the American people have been given pleasant-sounding justifications for this program, such as making the transition from an offense-dominated arms race to a defense-dominated arms race and building a nuclear shield to protect the American people from a nuclear attack. Such claims helped sell the program, even if they have little to do with reality.

The History of Anti–Ballistic Missile Weapons

The United States has been working on defenses against nuclear weapons since the early fifties, after the Soviets exploded their first atomic bomb in 1949 and their first hydrogen bomb not too long afterward. The work at that time was on air defenses, since that was the principal strategic weapon at the time. Efforts made on the development of air defenses were just an extension of those that had been developed for conventional air defense, since the important differences between defending against nuclear weapons and against conventional weapons was not appreciated at the time.

With the development of intercontinental ballistic missiles in the midfifties a focus was made on the development of an anti–ballistic missile (ABM) system, or ballistic missile defense. In the first development along this line, the air force had aircraft for interception that were assigned the task of area defense, while the army developed surface-to-air missiles that were assigned the task of terminal defense of civilian and military targets. Defense development soon became the exclusive responsibility of the army, however. It developed the Nike-Zeus system in the late fifties to provide an area defense, utilizing a single-layer mechanically steered radar.

It became apparent, however, that the Soviets had the capability for developing several countermeasures to this setup, such as the use of decoys and saturation attack to penetrate the defense. This project then gave way to the Nike-X system in the early sixties, which utilized low-altitude interception and more sophisticated radars. This new approach allowed a possible way of avoiding the problems of decoys, since these would burn up upon reentry into the atmosphere before the defense was reached. Sprint missiles were utilized in the system, which allowed for the faster acceleration necessary for a low-altitude interception.[6]

In the midfifties the Soviets started building air defenses, and that development went through several stages. However, it was not until the midsixties that they first developed a ballistic missile defense. This utilized the Galosh interceptor missile and phased-array and other early-warning radars and was deployed around Moscow, presumably to protect the national capital.

The deployment of the Galosh defense caused some concern within the Johnson administration and led to a decision in 1967 to deploy the Sentinel ABM system in the United States. This system had two missiles with nuclear warheads: the Spartan for high-altitude (exoatmospheric) interception of ballistic missiles, and the Sprint for endoatmospheric interception of ballistic missiles that penetrated the Spartan defense. This system was to provide an area defense to protect cities.

In the debate over the Sentinel, technological developments in radar, computers, and faster interceptors were taken as a strong motivation for the belief that the United States was ready for a major program of defensive weapons. On the other hand, a number of scientists pointed out the vulnerabilities of the system and how the system could be overwhelmed by the other side if it was determined to do so, such as by blacking out the radars with nuclear explosions. In addition, it was pointed out that the development of this system counteracted the notion of "mutually assured destruction," which had provided a certain basis for stability between the superpowers. Since the development of this defensive system would thus encourage offensive development by the other side, the tendency of defenses to accelerate the arms race began to be appreciated.

In 1969 President Nixon replaced the planned Sentinel with the slightly modified Safeguard. Funding for the Safeguard was debated in Congress that year, and it narrowly passed, with Vice-President Spiro Agnew breaking the tie vote in the Senate. The plans for Safeguard deployment were dropped in 1972 with the signing of the SALT I and ABM treaties. The ABM Treaty prohibited antiballistic systems, including certain supporting radars, with the exception of a defense of the national capital and a single missile field on each side. Each site was limited to 100 interceptors. (This treaty is discussed in more depth in Chapter 10.)[7]

After the signing of the ABM Treaty the United States initiated the building of a Safeguard defensive missile system to protect a Minuteman missile-silo field near Grand Forks, South Dakota, as allowed by the treaty. Development of this site proceeded for several years until it was decided in the midseventies that such a system would not be an effective defense, given Soviet countermeasures against it. The project was abandoned after $6 billion had been spent on it because it was assessed to be, like all the previous systems, ineffectual and basically worthless as a defense.

The Soviets have maintained their defense using Galosh missiles around Moscow, as provided by the treaty. Although several proponents of a new ABM system for the United States under SDI have pointed to the ABM system around Moscow as "the world's only ABM missile system," it is widely accepted (even by former Secretary of Defense Weinberger) that it is not an effective system.

A number of developments have been made in the technology of computers, lasers, particle beams, and space vehicles since the ABM Treaty. These developments provided the motivation for a number of people who were pushing the idea of space-based ballistic-missile defense in the late seventies. It was claimed that developments along these lines made possible a new approach to provide a ballistic-missile defense, despite the fact that all previous forms were worthless as a defense. Claims that the Soviets had made major advances in research and development along these lines were repeatedly made, and the implication of such advances supposedly was that we must make a major effort to catch up with them.

In 1979 Senator Malcolm Wallop of Wyoming urged Reagan to make missile defense an issue in the 1980 campaign for president, but it was not done. The same year, an MIT graduate student, Peter Hagelstein, on a prestigious Hertz Foundation Fellowship from Lawrence Livermore Laboratories and working on research at the labs, came up with a novel idea for an X-ray laser powered by a nuclear explosion. His focus was on the development of a laboratory X-ray laser, but he was asked to participate in Edward Teller's group investigating possible X-ray laser weapons powered by a nuclear explosion because of his knowledge of X-ray lasers. The group became very excited about the idea he introduced, strongly urging development. The project to develop the nuclear-explosion-powered X-ray laser was code-named Excalibur. The work of the group eventually led to the successful testing of the X-ray laser at the Nevada test site.[8] (Peter Hagelstein resigned from Lawrence Livermore Laboratories in 1986 because he objected to the weapons research, then returned as a part-time consultant in 1987 under the condition that he would only work on unclassified research unrelated to weapons.)

Edward Teller had several meetings with White House officials on the breakthrough in research on the nuclear-pumped X-ray laser from 1980 to 1982, including President Reagan in the fall of 1982. Others were also pushing the ideas of a missile defense based upon either General Graham's "high frontier" concept of a kinetic-energy-weapon defense or a chemical-laser defense. Pursuing a strategic-missile defense became public policy with the advent of the Strategic Defense Initiative.

After the Strategic Defense Initiative began in 1983, Roy Woodruff, director of weapons research at Lawrence Livermore Laboratories, was openly critical of the fact that Dr. Teller had exaggerated the capability and status of the X-ray laser to President Reagan in 1983, claiming it to be ready for the engineering phase of development. Thus the Strategic Defense Initiative may have been motivated by false information. Dr. Woodruff resigned from his position because of conflicts caused by his speaking out and was subsequently demoted at Lawrence Livermore. Dr. Woodruff brought the case to the University of California (which oversees the lab) in early 1987. The university appointed Dr. Woodruff in late 1987 to a new post as head of verification.[9]

Master Plans and Spending Trends

The Defense Department has been funding research on concepts that would be useful for space weapons since the midseventies. The Russian beam-weapon flap in 1977 provided motivation for the United States to further research on beam weapons. The U.S. Air Force Space Master Plan on space programs for the rest of this century, put out just before the Strategic Defense Initiative, discusses plans for development of space combat systems to be used for fighting in space.[10]

The rapid increase in military expenditures on space systems and space weapons is in line with this trend. For fiscal 1987 the Department of Defense spent over $16 billion in space research and development, compared to only about $9 billion spent by NASA. Of this $9 billion nearly $4 billion goes to the space shuttle program and $2 billion to replace the *Challenger,* which blew up in January 1986. But half of the shuttle missions are run for military purposes (which are paid out of the NASA budget rather than that of Defense). Thus the major push in space is for military uses. About three times as many resources are designated for military uses of space as for the civilian effort. (In fiscal 1981 the expenditures on civilian and military space efforts were about equal.)

Since 1980 a rapid growth has taken place in military space efforts, compared to a much slower growth in the civilian part of NASA. Initially the SDI program was growing the most rapidly, but congressional cuts soon limited this. These cuts caused former President Reagan to make a strong public plea at the fifth anniversary of the start of SDI for Congress to increase budgeted funds for SDI. Any unnecessary delay in the development and deployment of SDI was said to be "unconscionable."

The SDI program had funding rates of increase for the first few years that well exceeded most other programs funded by the federal government. The expense of researching and developing an ABM system, a low-level research program before SDI, was $0.9 billion for the first year of SDI. The funding for the program then increased rapidly for the first few years, as shown for the Department of Defense (DOD) requests and appropriations in Table 1.1. In addition to the DOD funding shown in the table, there has been a Department of Energy (DOE) funding appropriation of $200–$400 million per year.

Congress has put tighter reins on the program more recently. For example, an effort was made in the Senate for the fiscal 1988 budget to amend the growth in the program to the low rate to which many programs of the national budget are held. The proposed budget for that year of $5.8 billion (DOD and DOE) was trimmed by the Senate down to $4.5 billion. An effort was made to amend this to $3.7 billion, holding the increase to

Table 1.1. Department of Defense (DOD) and total SDI budget since its inception[a]

Fiscal Year	DOD Request	Increase (%)	DOD Approved	Increase (%)	DOE Approved	Total
1984	0.99		0.99			
1985	1.78	79	1.40	41	0.22	1.66
1986	3.72	166	2.76	97	0.29	3.05
1987	4.80	74	3.29	19	0.36	3.65
1988	5.35	63	3.61	10	0.35	3.96
1989	4.64[b]	29	3.71	3	0.24	3.95
1990	5.60	51	3.61	−3	0.21	3.82
1991	4.66	29				

[a]Billions of dollars proposed and approved
[b]The original request was for a $6.30 billion total budget, but that was reduced to a $5.00 billion request.

under 3%. The Senate vote for it was 50–50, and Vice-President George Bush broke the tie to kill the amendment. The House passed a cut to $3.5 billion, and the compromise between the House and Senate led to a total budget of $3.9 billion.

For fiscal 1989, a total of $6.7 billion was originally requested, but the request was cut to $5.0 billion because of cuts in the 5-year defense plan. Appropriations for 1989 were a total of $4.0 billion. The budget for fiscal 1990 was proposed at $5.9 billion by the Reagan administration but revised by the Bush administration to $4.9 billion. The compromise between the Senate and House led to a funding of $3.8 billion. This was the first reduction of SDI funding from the year before.

In the earlier years of the SDI program, a series of long-term budgets were projected for the "research" phase. The original goal was for the research phase of SDI to be 5 years at a cost of $26 billion. This soon became a plan of $33 billion for 6 years. A later version was 7 years for $44 billion. A 10-year $95 billion goal was also proposed. However, congressional cuts prevented these goals from being reached. Part of the motivation for the cuts have undoubtedly arisen from the 1985 Gramm-Rudman-Hollings Act, which requires multibillion-dollar cuts in the overall budget to reduce the deficit for each year.

Humanity's Choice

This country has finite resources. We have only a finite amount of money that can be used, a finite amount of skilled labor to deal with the science and technology issues, and a finite amount of technological resources that can be used in space. We must make choices between civilian uses of space and military uses of space. These involve choices between what is good in the long run for humanity in the space environment and weapons in that space environment.

With the significant increases in space concentration made and proposed by the military, it is useful to understand the difference between the militarization of space and the weaponization of space. *Militarization* refers to a large variety of the military uses of space, including communication satellites, spy satellites, treaty verification satellites, and early-warning satellites. Most of this is good for the nation because it helps ensure that other countries are keeping their treaties with us, warns us of possible nuclear attack, and ensures rapid communication needed by the military worldwide. It can help ensure nuclear stability, decreasing the chance of a nuclear war.

On the other hand the term *weaponization* has been used to refer to the means of using and placement of weapons in space. These can be of the form of capabilities of attacks into space using ground-based weapons as well as space-based weapons. Thus the undesirable aspect of the considerable military buildup in space is the developing and placing of weapons in space. The SDI defense fits into this category.

One example of this distinction is the difference between military satellites used for spying and satellites used as antisatellite weapons (ASATs). The first is an example of militarization of space, which serves a useful purpose—namely, warning us of a surprise attack or major arm movements that might lead to such an attack. The latter is a weaponization of space—the launching of satellites with weapons aboard. Weaponization conflicts with peaceful uses of space.

Goals of SDI

In an Office of Technology Assessment study of ballistic-missile defense technologies to be developed under the Strategic Defense Initiative, the goals of this program were set out. The idea of a population defense supported by the president was basically rejected as a goal (despite the fact that the president has repeated this as the goal many times). The goals were (in chronological order):[11]

1. Research to determine if there are defensive weapons that are cheaper than the offensive weapons needed to penetrate them.
2. A decision to develop these weapons for deployment.
3. A "transition stage" in which negotiations with the Soviets would allow for the defense deployment along with offensive-weapon reduction.
4. A final stage where offensive weapons are reduced to such low levels that the two countries cannot destroy each other with nuclear weapons.

These goals sound worthwhile on the surface. Are these the positive steps the United States needs to take to eliminate the nuclear threat? There are several questions that must be asked and answered before a conclusion can be drawn whether these goals are plausible, realistic, or attainable. These include questions such as the potential for inexpensive defenses; whether a "transition stage" is possible; whether the U.S. economy can withstand the costs of research, development, and deployment; whether these weapons will stabilize or destabilize tensions; and whether cheaper and more effective ways can be found to lessen or even eliminate the nuclear threat.

With the considerable offensive force reductions envisioned by this report, the requirements for an effective defense become less stringent, but the system will still have to work virtually perfectly at the reduced offensive levels to truly eliminate the threat of nuclear weapons. Is such a final state realistically possible without drastic nuclear weapon reductions and an improvement in tensions that still exist between the Soviet Union and the United States? And if such drastic reductions can be achieved, might there not be some other less expensive way to rid ourselves of the nuclear threat?

In the succeeding chapters the proposed space-based missile defense will be critically analyzed from scientific, political, economic, and arms-control perpectives. In Chapters 2–6 the scientific possibilities and barriers will be discussed, with realistic capabilities examined and weaknesses exposed. It will be shown why the United States may never come close to the goal of achieving any realistic population defense. Chapter 7 will then address the plan for early deployment that became the focus of SDI in 1987, along with the more recent ALPS (Accidental-Launch Protection System) and Brilliant Pebbles proposals.

In Chapters 8–10 the proposed systems will be analyzed from the perspective of the whole arms race, with arms-control questions and relevant treaties examined and potential dangers presented. It will be shown why the systems the president and other SDI officials envision can fuel an acceleration of the arms race and may counteract the hope of achieving the goal of the reduction of nuclear forces to a low level.

In Chapter 11 the effect of the SDI program on Europe and past U.S. efforts to get them involved in the program will be examined. Implications of deploying a strategic defense for the economy and the possibility of nuclear war will be examined in Chapter 12, along with a discussion of possible alternative ways for achieving nuclear disarmament and eliminating the nuclear threat.

Introduction to Missile Defense

Ballistic Missile Flight

In Figure 2.1 a typical trajectory (flight path) of an intercontinental ballistic missile (ICBM) launched from the Soviet Union toward the United States is shown. The trajectories of ICBMs are divided up into four phases. The first is the boost phase, the phase in which the stages of the missile (numbering 2 to 4) boost the missile out of the atmosphere and into space. This phase ends when all of the fuel of the missile

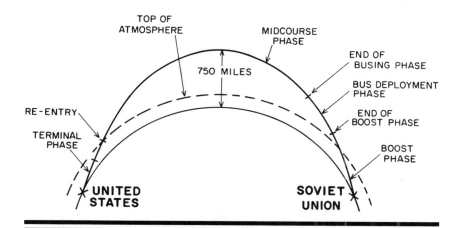

Fig. 2.1. The four phases of the flight of an ICBM from the Soviet Union to the United States.

has been spent and the boosting stages jettisoned, so that only the payload remains. It has been given all the energy and momentum it needs to reach the target before descending to ground level.

At the end of the boost phase, the missile enters the postboost phase, also known as the busing phase, where the multiple independently targeted reentry vehicles (also known as warheads), or MIRVs, are deployed (released from their carrier). Each of these warheads can be targeted to a certain location within the strike zone. During the postboost phase the bus can also deploy several thousand balloons, and the warheads can be hidden inside them. This phase ends when the bus deployment is complete.

Then the warheads enter the midcourse phase. During the midcourse phase they reach a maximum altitude of about 1,200 kilometers (750 miles) for the normal launch angle of 23° with respect to the Earth's surface (angle chosen for expending a minimum amount of fuel by the rocket). The warheads (reentry vehicles, or RVs) reenter the atmosphere toward the end of the midcourse, then proceed into the terminal phase where the bombs are activated and exploded.

The missile is most vulnerable during the boost phase, for at least three reasons. First, the missile can be rendered inoperative by damaging or exploding the fuel tanks of the booster, which is much easier to do than to counter the warheads after the boost phase is over; this causes the missile to go wildly off-course, and it is taken out of action. Second, missiles that are not taken out of action in the boost phase are MIRVed into as many as 10 independent warheads, so that after the boost phase it takes 10 hits to do what one could do during the boost phase. Third, after the missile is MIRVed, the individual warheads are much smaller than the boost-phase missile and are very hardened objects, designed to withstand the tough reentry conditions that involve heating of the warhead to very high temperatures due to atmospheric friction; thus they are much tougher to destroy.

However, the difficulty is that the boost phase is very short (and it can be made shorter, as will be discussed in later chapters). This creates considerable difficulty in having a totally effective boost-phase defense. For this reason, the approach being pursued in developing a strategic defense is to have a multilayered defense, with a boost-phase defense, one or two midcourse defenses, and a terminal defense. This means that the boost-phase defense must be 90% effective just to break even—that is, to have only as many objects to counter after the boost phase as were present when the boost phase started.

Submarine-launched ballistic missiles (SLBMs) have four shorter phases. They are launched from some spot in the ocean, which will be considerably closer to the target than the land-based ICBMs. To use the strategic defense against SLBMs, the United States must have satellites for global surveillance, so that a launch from a submarine from any place on the globe can be observed very quickly, and also have a defense in a suitable location to counter the SLBMs. The length of time of the SLBM ballistic trajectory is shorter than that for ICBMs, as short as 10 minutes.

Defense Schemes

A number of schemes have been proposed for ballistic missile defense in the various flight stages of the missiles. These include the following: (1) laser-beam weapons, (2) particle-beam weapons, (3) kinetic-energy projectiles and railguns, and (4) homing rockets.

Lasers have come into common usage in science and engineering for a variety of applications. However, laser-beam weapons will require lasers that are much more powerful than the ones that we have today. For readers not familiar with lasers it is useful to give an intuitive idea of what lasers are (see Appendix 2, which has a discussion of the scientific principles by which a laser works). Lasers are sources of light that are both *coherent* and *monochromatic* (explained below). The laser beams have a minimal rate of spreading in width when they move out from their source. The types of lasers that are proposed for strategic defense must produce light beams of great power by making the light intensity at the source very strong.

The idea of *coherence* can be understood if one looks at the light beam shone onto a white wall or screen. One sees in the light pattern rings where the light intensity is darker, separated by rings where the light is brighter. This is produced by interference. The light waves coming from the source are not in phase with one another. Some waves in the beam partially or totally cancel one another out by destructive interference, producing the dark rings. Others reinforce one another since the light waves are in phase with one another, producing the brighter rings. Most sources of light have this property and are said to be *incoherent*. (An analogy can be drawn to two people pushing a heavy object. If they push against each other, all of their energy is wasted, and the box does not move. On the other hand, if they push in the same direction, their forces are added, and a greater intensity of work is achieved.)

With a laser, however, the individual waves making up the beam are all added in phase with one another. The result is that there are virtually no interference rings or waves canceling each other. This increases the total brightness of the beam as well as the power that the laser can emit.

The term *monochromatic* means that a single frequency of light is emitted. This is in contrast with ordinary light, which has a broad range of frequencies (several colors or a spectrum running over a color range). The result of the process is to create a beam that is bright and forms a pencil-thin beam with minimum spreading. This is to be compared with an ordinary flashlight in which light comes out in a wide cone. These two characteristics of a laser—coherence and monochromaticity—allow the laser-beam intensity to be very great, so the laser emits a powerful beam of light. These properties have made lasers attractive for numerous applications, including the potential use of powerful lasers as weapons (the basic mechanisms by which a laser-beam weapon destroys a missile are summarized in Appendix 3).

The original emphasis under SDI was on the use of lasers for defense, because these are the most promising for a boost-phase defense (this changed with the move toward the early deployment of a first-phase defense before laser defenses are developed, to be discussed in Chapter 7). Since the boost phase is the optimum time for the use of a missile defense, more research has gone into boost-phase applications. The reason that lasers are most attractive for a boost-phase defense is that the boost-phase time is so short—currently 4–5 minutes for Soviet missiles and less than 3 minutes for our missiles, but future technology developments can reduce this to under 1 minute. Thus the defense will need a very fast response to be able to detect the attack and effectively counter a very large percentage of the missiles in this short time. The use of homing rockets and kinetic-energy projectiles may be too slow, but laser weapons may act much faster. Particle beams have also been proposed for this phase but will require longer development and may face more difficulties than a laser defense. The approaches under investigation for a boost phase will be discussed in the next chapter.

Proposed particle-beam weapons would use intense beams of particles (such as neutral hydrogen atoms) moving at a high velocity (high energy). When these energetic particles impact with matter (such as the surface of a missile) at sufficient energy, they can cause major destruction. The beams would be produced by accelerators, similar to ones used in nuclear and particle physics research to examine the general structure of very small-scale units of matter through high-energy scattering.

Kinetic-energy projectiles are undergoing research and development for use in the midcourse stage of the defense. These are objects sent out at very high velocity to produce a devastating impact on their target just as bullets in a rifle do. The kinetic-energy objects are larger than bullets and will be moving around 1,000 times as fast, as will be necessary in order for them to destroy their targets. Lighter-weight versions of these are called *hypervelocity objects,* and they can be used to destroy shielding in the form of balloons that will be used to hide the warheads in the midcourse phase (discussed in more depth in Chapter 4). A type of gun that can shoot these objects through the use of electromagnetic forces is known as a *railgun*.

A *homing rocket* is a rocket that will explode when it impacts its target. These are small rockets that have a computerized homing mechanism. The rockets are launched to a particular position that is determined to be the approximate target zone. When the rockets reach the target zone, the homing mechanism surveys the immediate vicinity and determines the precise target location. It homes in on the target, making corrections on the way as needed, then explodes upon reaching the determined target. This homing mechanism provides for very high accuracy. Of course, there is no guarantee that what the rocket determines to be the target is the true target, so the rocket could destroy the wrong target.

The application of these defense schemes to the development of a ballistic-missile defense for the various stages of target missiles will be analyzed in the next two chapters.

Boost-Phase
Intercept Systems

Several concepts have been proposed and investigated on the use of high-powered laser and particle beams (directed-energy weapons), as well as homing rockets (kinetic-energy weapons), to intercept ICBMs during the boost phase of their launch. Lasers appear to provide the most promising method for rapidly hitting the target in the short boost phase. During the boost phase the missiles are much more vulnerable than the warheads that they deploy in later phases, so a powerful laser beam could be used to counter them.

Chemical Lasers in Low Earth Orbit

The chemical laser is a high-powered laser that emits at infrared wavelengths. The chemical reaction pumps the laser, and the most promising form is one in which hydrogen or deuterium (a form of heavy hydrogen) reacts with fluorine, forming hydrogen or deuterium fluoride. The operating principles of the chemical laser are discussed in Appendix 4. There is also a good description of chemical and gas dynamic lasers in an article by Tsipis.[1]

The infrared beam created by the hydrogen fluoride laser is absorbed over short distances inside the Earth's atmosphere, so it must be used outside the atmosphere for space-based defense applications. This typically confines the laser beam to an altitude above 100 kilometers, although the phenomenon of "bleaching" the atmosphere in the path of the laser beam might allow it to extend 10 or 20 kilometers lower. The shorter-wavelength deuterium fluoride laser beam is not as strongly absorbed and could extend to much lower altitudes.

The laser would be based on a defense station in low Earth orbit a few hundred miles above the Earth's surface to attack and destroy the missiles during their short boost phase. Satellites with the defense lasers will revolve about the Earth about every 1.5 hours. During its revolution the Earth is rotating, so that at the completion of a revolution about the Earth, the satellite does not return over the surface region where the orbit started. For polar orbits, for example, it takes a day (a complete Earth rotation) before the satellite is back over the same surface region again (see Figure 3.1). Thus, it is not possible for the satellites to be accessible to the Soviet ICBM fields more than a fraction of the day. They are accessible to the Soviet missile fields for only a few orbits of the day, and the access times last only a fraction of the 1.5-hour period for the orbit.

Several defense satellites in orbit are necessary for every one that is over the Soviet missile fields at any given time, and many satellites will be needed over the Soviet missile fields simultaneously in order to cover the missiles. Defense satellites that are not over the land-based missile fields could be used to cover all of the oceans from which submarines containing SLBMs can be stationed by the Soviets if the defense satellite orbits are uniformly spaced, but boost-phase countering of SLBMs with this defense may not be possible.

If the purpose of the defense is only to cover the ICBM fields, the coverage can be optimized. The inclination of the orbits with respect to the equator determines the number of orbits during which the satellites are accessible to the missile fields. For example, the polar orbits in Figure 3.1 are at 90° inclination to the equator, while the other set of orbits is at an inclination of 45°. The latter set has greater accessibility to the Soviet ICBM fields. The orbits would be about 60° from the equator to optimize coverage of the ICBM fields. This optimization reduces the number of satellites required by a factor of about 3.

How many defense satellites are needed, then, to cover the Soviet missiles? This depends upon several factors, such as the power and efficiency of the laser, the chance that a firing of the laser will hit the target, the "slew and settle" time (time necessary to retarget the laser after firing), and the number and configuration of Soviet missiles the defense must counter.

The initial goal of the Strategic Defense Initiative was to build a 2-million-watt laser for the defense. However, later studies have shown that laser powers of 20–100 megawatts will be needed. In the 1987 study by the American Physical Society it was concluded that the power of the hydrogen fluoride chemical lasers would have to be increased by a factor of at least 20 over what is currently available and meet an acceptable beam

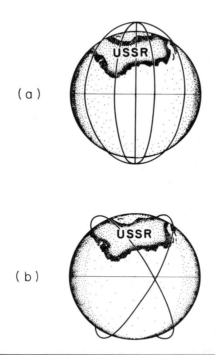

(a)

(b)

Fig. 3.1. (a) Constellation of polar (90° inclination to equator) satellite orbits around the Earth. As the Earth rotates, the coverage of Soviet ICBM fields shifts from one orbit to the next. This constellation provides global coverage to counter SLBMs as well, with maximum coverage near the poles. (b) Orbits inclined just above 45° give greater coverage of Soviet ICBM fields. If optimum coverage of the ICBM fields is desired (not global coverage), the orbit inclination would be about 60°. [After Ashton Carter, Ballistic Missile Defense (Washington, D.C.: U.S. Government Printing Office, 1985), p. 29]

quality for use in the defense. Attaining this will require innovative new technologies.[2]

Currently the Soviets have 1,400 ICBMs, but could have a future number around 3,000 (later chapters discuss how a missile defense will encourage the Soviets to expand their offensive force). Estimates of other factors can be made based on what we can reasonably hope to achieve in the future. In calculations made by Richard Garwin it was determined that for 3,000 ICBMs based in a clustered configuration with a reasonable 100-second boost-phase time and an orbiting laser of 25 megawatts of power with an optimistic defensive slew and settle time of 0.5 seconds, a minimum of 500 satellites will be needed. This assumes a very high accuracy of the targeting (Appendix 5 contains a more detailed examination of these numbers).

If the laser targeting error is one part in 1 million, this number will increase to 1,500. The calculation also assumes an optimal satellite configuration to cover the Soviet missile fields. If the goal was for a uniform global coverage to also defend against SLBMs based at any location in the oceans, these numbers would have to be increased by a factor of 3.

The cost of a defense satellite with chemical lasers approaches $1 billion. Conservative Defense Department estimates have put the satellite cost at a few hundred million, while a study of SDI costs determined it to be about $1.75 billion.[3] Thus the development and building of such a fleet of satellites would approach $1 trillion! This would be in addition to the costs for the midcourse and terminal defenses that would have to accompany it.

There are two serious operational problems associated with having a fleet of these satellites in orbit to counter Soviet missiles. The first is that the laser systems will probably be massive and bulky, with large tanks of hydrogen or deuterium and fluorine. The size and weight of the systems will likely require a new type of shuttle with powerful engines to transport them into orbit. A heavy-lift vehicle (the Advanced Launch System) for such space deployment is planned to be ready around the year 2000. The cost of the fuel alone for launching this defense could easily run $20 billion.

The second problem involves the gases used in the laser. The gases could contaminate the optics used for the laser. The hydrogen fluoride used in the laser could damage the optical components and is quite corrosive to the laser's gas-piping system, so that they would disintegrate over time unless material becomes available for the pipes and optics that is impervious to it. Otherwise, these systems on the defense station would have to be periodically changed, which would be an involved task for the orbiting satellites.

The X-ray Laser and the Pop-up Defense

The X-ray-laser defensive weapon is a more recent concept, and much of the research associated with it is classified. Achieving the intensities of radiation required at these short wavelengths demands a very large power source. The prodigious amount needed can be attained only in a nuclear explosion, which serves as the power source (see Figure 3.2). The explosion destroys the defensive system, so the power must be generated in the extremely short time between the ignition of the explosion and the disintegration of the laser structure (a few billionths of a second). The laser can be fired only once.

The radiation from the X-ray laser emerges in a narrow cone, spreading out from the source. The angle of the spreading depends on the wavelength and the width of the lasing rod, so the width is chosen to minimize this angle. This angle and the efficiency with which the power of the nuclear explosion is converted into laser radiation determines the effective gain of the laser. This gain, which represents the factor at which the radiation intensity can be increased over that from an ordinary nuclear explosion can be as high as 100 million (see Appendix 6 for a discussion of the details of this laser).

Deployment of X-ray lasers on space platforms in near-Earth orbit, in the same manner as the proposed deployment of chemical-laser stations, presents a special difficulty that does not occur with chemical lasers: The nuclear explosion and the destructive power in the X-ray laser beam at one station is potentially destructive of vital systems on nearby stations

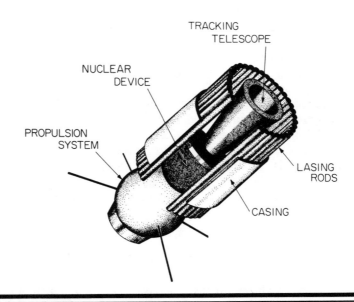

Fig. 3.2. Basic components of an X-ray laser.

that are not yet exploded, because of the high-powered X-rays as well as the long range of the blast and the electromagnetic pulse (sudden intense waves) created by the nuclear explosion. This drawback is in addition to the same problems encountered for chemical lasers in low Earth orbit: Several satellites would be required for every one that is present at any given time over the Soviet missile fields. More satellites would be needed for an X-ray-laser defense than for the chemical-laser defense since the X-ray laser is used only once whereas the chemical laser can repeatedly fire and retarget. Thus low-Earth-orbit deployment is not a viable basing mode for X-ray lasers in a boost-phase defense.

The mode that was initially proposed under SDI for the basing of X-ray lasers is that of the so-called pop-up defense. In this mode the defense stations would be based on submarines in the ocean, to be popped up into space by rockets upon warning of a Soviet ICBM attack. This option is not a feasible one for chemical lasers because those systems are too large, and launching them on rockets would considerably reduce the repetition of the laser firing available to them on satellites. On the other hand, the X-ray-laser payloads are relatively lightweight and fire only once, so launching them from submarines initially appeared plausible.

The problem of launching the missiles from submarines in an ocean that is separated from the ICBM launching sites in the Soviet Union is the curvature of the Earth. Furthermore, the beam effectively cannot travel through the atmosphere. As a result the defense rockets must rise to a substantial distance into space in order to target the Soviet-launched ICBMs with the laser beam in a direct line of sight over the atmosphere (see Figure 3.3). The nearest point to most of the Soviet missile fields that the submarines could be placed is in the Indian Ocean. In that location the rockets would have to rise about 1,250 miles (2,000 kilometers) to be able to access all of the Soviet ICBMs in their boost phase for a boost-phase time of 150 seconds.[4]

The time and fuel required for a rocket to rise this distance are critical factors in this defense. The time necessary for the defense rocket to rise to a sufficient height is in addition to the time required for detection of the ICBM launch by our early-warning satellites, the decision time required for initiating the defensive launch sequence, the rise time of the submarines if necessary, and the firing time of the missiles. These additional times will further shorten the time available to destroy the missiles in the boost phase. This means that the requirement for fuel would be significantly increased.

For a Soviet boost-phase time of only 100 seconds, the rockets would have to rise in about 50 seconds to counter the missiles in their boost phase, allowing a short time for detecting, alerting, possible submarine

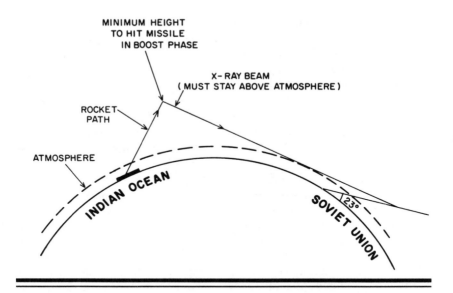

Fig. 3.3. Rise of the X-ray-laser rocket necessary to hit the Soviet ICBM, given the Earth's curvature and the inability of the laser beam to penetrate the atmosphere.

surfacing, and rocket-launch preparation to counter the attack. To counter missiles from Soviet fields around 50° latitude north, the defense rockets would need to accelerate nearly 900 meters per second squared, which would require a fuel mass of 7,000 times the payload interceptor. If this payload could be made as light as 100 kilograms (220 pounds), then 700,000 kilograms (1.54 million pounds) of fuel would be needed! (See the calculation and discussion of these numbers in Appendix 7.)

The boost-phase time of present Soviet ICBMs is 180–300 seconds, compared to 150–180 seconds for U.S. ICBMs. However, the time for the Soviet boost phase can be shortened as their technology reaches the state of present U.S. technology by going to fast-burn boosters, similar to what was used on U.S. Sprint missiles. The Soviets could shorten their missile boost-phase time to under 50 seconds, under the minimum time necessary for a pop-up defense. The problems of the prodigious amount of fuel required for the necessary rapid acceleration, and the potential of the Soviets' installing fast-burn boosters in future missiles appear to be insurmountable, implying that an X-ray laser used for a boost-phase defense will be rendered completely ineffective with future Soviet technology.

The X-ray laser also has potential midcourse applications, which will be discussed in the next chapter. The technology of the X-ray laser still requires substantial development for any type of defensive use. In the American Physical Society study it was concluded that it is yet to be demonstrated whether it is possible to make a useful X-ray laser for a missile defense.[5]

Orbiting Mirrors and Excimer or Free-Electron Laser

The third concept being researched is that of a ground-based laser operating at high frequencies (probably the ultraviolet) that can penetrate the Earth's atmosphere. The laser beam would be relayed to orbiting mirrors that would target the missiles. The original idea was to use an *excimer* laser (which operates in the ultraviolet), although a new laser still in the experimental stage, the *free-electron laser,* is considered to have greater long-term prospects for this purpose. The laser beam of the free-electron laser is amplified by a stream of energetic electrons that are continually accelerated, and it can be tuned to any frequency (the operating principles of the excimer laser and free-electron laser are discussed in Appendices 8 and 9).

This scheme requires a primary mirror in geosynchronous orbit over the United States (one that revolves about the Earth at the same rate as the Earth's rotation, thus hovering over one spot on the Earth). For such an orbit the mirror would have to be 22,000 miles from the Earth (see Figure 3.4). The laser stations on the ground would send their beams up to this geosynchronous mirror, which would reflect them down to low-Earth-orbiting mirrors covering the Soviet missile launch sites, and these mirrors would reflect the beams to the targeted missiles. Several hundred of these low-orbit mirrors would be required because of the Earth's rotation.

There are a number of potential difficulties with this scheme. Some of the problems involve phenomena that can occur in the Earth's atmosphere to degrade the laser beam. Atmospheric turbulence will cause the beam to spread out and wander in a random fashion. The high-powered laser beam can heat the air that the beam passes through, causing the heated air to expand, pulling the laser beam with it.

The laser beam can also ionize the atmosphere in the beam path (causing the outer electrons of the air molecules to escape, leaving the molecules as positively charged ions), and this ionization process will absorb energy from the beam. Water vapor and dust in the atmosphere can absorb energy from the laser beam, decreasing the amount of power that reaches the mirror.

There is a promising potential solution to correct one of these diffi-

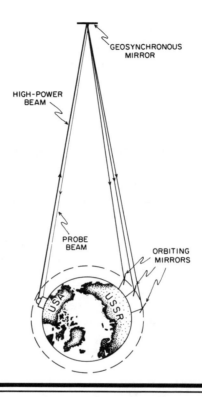

Fig. 3.4. Orbiting-mirror defense with ground-based laser and geosynchronous mirror to transfer the beam to low-Earth-orbiting satellites covering the Soviet missile fields. The probe beam is used to correct for atmospheric distortions in the high-power laser beam.

culties: atmospheric density fluctuations associated with atmospheric turbulence. The solution is to correct the distortion caused in the wavefront by these effects by a method known as *adaptive optics*. However, this is only one of several problems created by the atmosphere, and most of them cannot be corrected.[6]

The problem of sending a high-powered beam up to a geosynchronous mirror and reflecting it down to the low-Earth-orbit mirrors has serious difficulties besides the degradation of the beam in the Earth's atmosphere. The Earth-based laser stations will require tremendous fuel reserves. Furthermore, one such station will not be adequate because a cloudy day would effectively disable a laser site. Clouds absorb the energy of the beam. Since clouds are always moving, there is no purpose in trying to burn a hole through the clouds with the laser beam. Thus we will need several laser stations well separated in location so that there will be at least one that is not in an overcast area. (And even then there will be a small chance that all of them are cloud-covered.)

Excimer lasers that exist today do not approach the power levels that are required for this defense system. The American Physical Society study concluded that the power of these lasers needs to be increased by a factor of at least 10,000. In addition, several advances in technology are required to produce the necessary beam quality. Free-electron lasers appear to have greater promise for achieving the high powers required, but their earlier development stage precludes an accurate estimate of their potential.[7]

The mirror out at geosynchronous orbit will need to be about 5–10 meters in diameter (depending on the diffraction of the laser beam). In order to reflect the beam at that distance down to mirrors at low altitude, a virtually flawless mirror with very low surface scatter and extremely accurate optics will be required. We are presently far from having the technology that will be required. Even so-called super-reflecting mirrors have some imperfections in the way they scatter light, so that they inevitably degrade the beam they are scattering. A small defect or disturbing influence on the mirror system could substantially throw off the accuracy of the reflection over the distances the beams must travel.

Furthermore, the geosynchronous mirror must be able to sustain the very high-powered laser beams that it has to reflect. The high power levels required can cause distortion of the reflective surface. All mirrors have some absorption of the light beam that they are reflecting. Even a minute absorption of the powerful incoming beam will cause substantial heating, and significant distortion of the aiming and focusing characteristics will result unless adequate rapid-cooling systems are installed on the mirror. Because minute amounts of absorption and other physical limitations cannot be avoided, it is not clear that such a mirror could be developed in the foreseeable future. As a result of the very high-quality optics that would be required and the significant research and development necessary before sufficiently powerful free-electron or excimer lasers are available, such a mirror defense is unlikely to be available for several decades.

Lasers of the high power levels needed must await developments in future research and technology, and it is difficult to estimate the price tag on them when and if they are developed. However, an estimate on the power required for fueling the lasers and the possible costs can be made. In Appendix 10 the power levels needed for this defense are estimated.

The estimate made for the minimum power that will be needed assumes a 10-meter-diameter geosynchronous mirror, the Soviets' present number of 1,400 ICBMs, that the only atmospheric propagation effects on the laser beam is the scattering off the air molecules (this kind of scattering of sunlight gives the sky its blue color), that the laser stations are at high altitude (e.g., on a mountain top) to minimize this scattering, that 20% of the destructive power actually ends up on the missiles after it leaves the atmosphere (after traversing over 40,000 miles), and that a 25% efficiency of free-electron lasers is achieved (present excimer lasers are much less efficient). This minimum power required to knock out the missiles would be about 200 billion watts, approximately the current power consumption of the United States. Assuming the lowest cost at which present nuclear generators can generate this power ($1,000/kilowatt), this power would cost about $200 billion. Developing power generators required for this task alone will be a demanding task.

The cost for the lasers and other auxiliaries (the "perfect" geosynchronous mirror and the orbiting mirrors) will add to the costs for power generation that have been estimated. (Of course, this would be only one phase of a multiple-phase defense.) The cost for the power generation alone at current generation rates is $150 million for every $25-million missile that the defense destroys. The cost per missile will be significantly greater than this when the other costs of the boost-phase defense are included. (The consequences of having such relative economies of the defense versus those of the offensive force that it defends against are examined in Chapters 6 and 8.)

The assumptions used for the calculation of the necessary power depend on an estimate of what can reasonably be produced in optical technology in the foreseeable future. If more modest standards are made in this technology, or if the Soviets expand their offensive force, the power needed will increase. For example, if the Soviets expand their force to 3,000 missiles and 90% of the power is lost in the long-range targeting of the missiles, the power required goes up to 900 billion watts. This would cost $900 billion at the rate of $1,000/watt of generation. On the other hand, future developments in power sources may decrease the cost of generating the large amounts of power needed. Suppose the cost of power production is reduced a factor of 10, reducing the cost to only $90 billion. This is still a cost of $30 million per $25-million missile taken out for the fuel alone. It appears that an orbiting-mirror defense will be very expensive even if the technology needed for the laser and the mirror can be developed.

Energetic Particle Beams

Another type of energy source that is being investigated for a boost-phase attack on missiles is that of particle beams. These can be produced by high-energy accelerators. Particle beams have an advantage over laser beams in that they can penetrate deeper into their target than laser beams and would be more difficult to shield against than laser beams (see the discussion of missile shielding in Chapter 6). On the other hand, there are some difficulties in a defense using particle beams that are not faced with laser beams.

The idea initially considered along this line in the 1970s was the use of charged-particle beams, particularly beams of ions (atoms with a deficiency or excess of electrons). However, the difficulty with charged particle-beams is that the particles making up the beam gyrate around the Earth's magnetic-field lines. More importantly, there are always small local fluctuations of the magnetic fields that are not predictable. Thus if an ion beam is fired at a target that is a significant distance away, the beam will miss because the magnetic-field fluctuations send the beam too far astray from the target. Furthermore, charged-particle beams tend to diverge very rapidly as they propagate out, quickly losing their power concentration because of the electrostatic repulsion of the beam particles.[8]

Experiments have been made using laser beams to help guide electron beams to allow them to stay together longer.[9] By 1987 experiments had demonstrated that the laser beams can guide the particle beams up to 100 meters. This is not feasible for ion beams because the energy of divergence in the ions and their orbit sizes are much too large for the laser beam. The effective distance for the laser-beam guidance would have to increase to several hundred kilometers (a factor of 10,000) before this technique becomes viable for use in a defensive weapon.

Because of the problems with a defense using charged-particle beams, more emphasis has been placed on the use of neutral beams. These can be produced by first accelerating ion beams, then attaching electrons (positive ions) or stripping excess electrons (for negative ions) before they leave the beam chamber. However, these beams cannot be used inside the atmosphere (below about 150 kilometers' altitude) because there they quickly ionize back to ion beams again and scatter from their destination. They can be useful only in space.

In Appendix 11 an estimate is made of the minimum power required to counter the current number of Soviet ICBMs, which is about 100 billion watts. This is about half the current power consumption rate in the United States, and it must be continually generated for about 50 seconds for a 100-second boost-phase time.

If there are 500 satellites over the Soviet missile fields at the time of launch (which will require over 1,500 satellites), then the accelerator on each of these satellites would require about 100 million watts of power. Both the problem of developing accelerators with power and auxiliary systems for use in satellites and that of launching them into orbit will be enormous jobs. Just maintaining the accelerators based on satellites would be a continuous major task. The power needed would run about $100 billion if the cost is the same as the lower-cost nuclear-generator sources of power today, at $1,000 per kilowatt. Major advances will need to be made in power generation with significant reductions in cost to make this defense affordable.

Although it is possible that neutral beams could be used in the future for a boost-phase defense if several technologies could be developed, they may be rendered ineffective by a nuclear explosion in the atmosphere at about 20–30 miles' altitude because the explosion would send enough atmosphere out into near-Earth space to cause the beams to ionize. This same countermeasure ("heaving" the atmosphere) may also be used against the X-ray-laser weapons because the X-rays are absorbed in a thin layer of air. However, particle beams are stopped even in air sufficiently tenuous that the X-ray-laser beam can pass through (see the calculation regarding the effect of this explosion in Appendix 12). Thus useful particle-beam weapons may not be feasible in the foreseeable future unless ways of dealing with this countermeasure are developed.

Homing Rockets on Satellites in Low Earth Orbit

Homing rockets are launched toward a given destination where the target is determined approximately to lie, then use artificial intelligence capabilities to search the target zone and determine more precisely where the target is (a weapon with such capabilities is commonly called a smart weapon). A homing rocket may identify the correct target or may identify something else as the target, but once it has made that choice, it sets its course to that target, making any midcourse corrections needed, and explodes when the determined target is reached.

Homing rockets are much slower than laser and particle beams in reaching their target and must destroy most of the missiles in the 1- to 2-minute boost phase. The fact that their velocity is significantly slower than laser or particle beams (around 10 kilometers per second) gives them an important disadvantage in a boost-phase defense. Furthermore, when in the atmosphere, infrared radiation generated by atmospheric friction is much greater than the infrared emission of the distant missiles needed to guide the homing rocket toward its target, so they would need to target boosters after the boosters exit the atmosphere. Possible advantages of homing rockets over beam weapons are (1) several can be launched from a single satellite and (2) their homing characteristics allow them constantly to adjust errors in their targeting.

An experiment using homing rockets to counter a missile, the Homing Overlay Experiment, was carried out in June 1984. An ICBM with a dummy warhead was launched from Vandenberg Air Force Base and tracked by radar on an island at Kaena Point. The homing rocket was launched from the Kwajalein missile range which used initial radar tracking to initiate its own tracking. It intercepted and destroyed the dummy warhead from the ICBM. The final velocity of the homing rocket was 9 kilometers a second before interception.[10]

The Delta mission in September 1986 was a follow-up experiment on the use of a homing rocket to intercept a missile. This experiment used a Delta missile that has some characteristics similar to Soviet missiles and an SDI homing vehicle that was successful in destroying its target. The Delta missile was initially tracked from its plume, and a set of trackers was used for the kill vehicle to home in on its target. The collision occurred after the Delta had reached its second stage, and the two vehicles were a maximum distance of 120 miles apart before interception.[11]

Although these preliminary tests have proved successful, several developments are necessary, and limitations restrict the viability of a boost-phase defense based on homing rockets. Homing rockets with terminal velocities of 10 kilometers per second will travel less than 1,000 kilometers in a 100-second boost-phase time. Considering the time necessary for detection of the missile launch, preparation for the rocket launch, and acceleration of the rocket to its maximum speed, the rocket may only have a 500-kilometer range in the 100-second boost phase.

Each homing rocket will generally take out only one missile in a boost-phase defense. Thus space-based boost-phase defense rockets with only this range would require a concentration of homing rockets that is considerably greater than the required number of lasers in a chemical-laser defense. By putting 10 homing rockets in each satellite, it may be possible to get the number of satellites required for an effective boost-phase defense down to a few thousand. Faster homing rockets could alleviate some of these restrictions, but the mass of fuel needed increases exponentially with the terminal velocity of the rocket. The significantly increased weight of the rocket creates more problems than the increased terminal velocity solves.

One of the major problems for a defense with homing rockets is the options that can be used on the missiles to lead the homing mechanism astray, preventing the homing rocket from destroying its actual target. It is fairly inexpensive for the Soviets to use a variety of decoy missiles and decoy devices that simulate the plume of a missile. They can also install "antisimulator" devices on the real missiles to make them appear the same as the decoys. The effectiveness of the defense will depend critically on how sensitive the homing systems are in discriminating fake from real signals, and conversely, on how well the Soviet decoy signals simulate real signals, as well as how good the real missiles are in "antisimulating" minor erratic decoy behavior.

If the defense is not effective in screening out the decoys when large numbers of decoys are launched with the missiles, it becomes ineffective in its ability to counter the missiles in their boost phase. However, the difficulty is that no matter how sensitive or accurate our homing mechanisms are, we can never be sure they cannot be foiled by Soviet decoy techniques since we cannot be sure how good the Soviet decoy simulations are or what form they will take.

The cost of a boost-phase defense utilizing homing rockets will be addressed in Chapter 7, which is devoted to the planned deployment of a Phase I SDI defense based on kinetic weapons rather than directed-energy weapons.

Midcourse and Terminal Interception

After the boost phase ends, the missile bus begins to deploy the multiple independently targeted reentry vehicles (MIRVs), or warheads. Each missile surviving the boost-phase defense multiplies, releasing up to 10 warheads (a future number could be 20 or 30). These warheads are hardened to withstand extreme heat and physical stress, and are significantly more difficult to destroy. Boost-phase defenses are generally not adequate for this task since it will require 10–100 times more power intensity to destroy the warheads. On the other hand, the advantage for the defense is that there is more time available. Thus it is not necessary to deliver the destructive energy to the targets at the very high speeds that laser and particle-beam weapons can provide for defense in the short boost phase.

When the individual warheads are MIRVed, large numbers of balloons and other penetration aids will also be deployed to screen the warheads. Since the warheads are now in free space, balloons follow the same ballistic trajectory as the warheads. The missiles can carry 20 balloons per warhead, so for a launch of 1,400 ICBMs that are unimpeded in the boost phase, 280,000 balloons could be deployed. Warheads can be hidden inside the balloons. Decoys deployed with the warheads can also be hidden in the balloons. Now the defense must either destroy all of the balloons to reveal which ones contain the warheads or use some detection mechanism to determine which balloons have warheads in them. The warheads must be destroyed after they have been located.

Midcourse and terminal phase defense techniques for locating the warheads, discriminating them from decoys, and countering are undergoing research and development. These will be examined.

Post-Boost-Phase Defense

At the end of the boost phase, the defense must be much more powerful to counter the payload of the missiles. Although boost-phase defenses will generally not be adequate for this purpose, the defense may still be useful in interfering with the busing process. The bus contains an inertial guidance system (for proper orientation in the busing process), and the reentry vehicles released contain *thrusters* (small rocket engines) that are used for independent targeting. The defense can damage the bus and throw off the targeting. In general, however, it will add little to the effectiveness of the defense in stopping the missiles. In addition, the busing process can be made very short in response to a missile defense, leading to very quick release of the decoys, balloons, and warheads.

Countering the warheads (released and about to be released) will usually require defenses planned for the midcourse. Use of the midcourse defense requires transmission of the boost-phase tracking data over to the midcourse tracking system (the Space-Based Surveillance and Tracking System, or SSTS, currently being developed). The midcourse defense must locate the warheads and decoys, attempt to determine which are real warheads, and proceed to counter them. This will probably take longer than future post-boost-phase times.

If the targets can be located before the midcourse phase begins, early countering success by the midcourse defense will have the advantage of being able to destroy more than one warhead. However, this will most probably only destroy a small percentage of the warheads. An effective defense after the boost phase must be one that can destroy most of the warheads in the midcourse phase of the missiles.

Midcourse Discrimination

Several proposals are being investigated for dealing with the problem of discriminating balloons that contain the warheads in midcourse. The first is a passive discrimination technique, using infrared detectors. The detectors would look for the evidence of the infrared radiation from the warheads. The infrared radiation of warheads is much smaller than that for missiles and arises from thruster burn and the residual heat that would still be with the warheads from the heating that occurs in the boost phase (the very hot booster engines will inevitably heat the payload, and some residual heat will remain when this missile reaches the midcourse phase).

However, the offense could counter the detectors by adding small heaters in the empty balloons that would also give off low-level infrared rays. This technique will mask the real warheads if the detectors are then unable to discriminate between the balloons with and those without warheads.

There is an additional method for masking the infrared signatures of real warheads. That is to use some high-resistance material such as mylar on the surface. This will absorb most of the infrared radiation signature given off by the warhead, so the infrared sensor cannot detect the infrared signal to home in on the warhead. When this is combined with the use of small heaters, there is little chance to discriminate the real warheads by this technique. With these countermeasures, infrared detection would be unsuccessful as a discrimination technique.

One thing that the infrared detection can still be useful for is tracking the balloons. It will be necessary for the defense to monitor where all balloons are until it determines which balloons have the warheads, and the infrared signature of the balloons could be used for this purpose. However, the infrared signature is weak and will be partially masked by natural infrared emissions from the Earth, so this may not provide a complete tracking system for the balloons.

Since passive discrimination will not be adequate, interactive discrimination techniques must be developed. One method for discrimination is to test each balloon for a warhead, using a neutral beam of energetic particles (see Figure 4.1). The defense would then analyze the particles emitted from any object in the balloon by a separate detector. There are two important processes producing particles that can be detected: the simple scattering of particles in the beam from the warhead or decoy, and energetic neutrons produced by a small amount of fission that the particles induce inside warheads. The fission does not cause the warhead to explode since the fissionable material in the bomb is separated to keep it below the critical mass that would be needed for a chain reaction. Thus the fission dies out immediately after the brief time during which the beam interacts with the bomb.

An important question on the use of neutral particle beams to detect which balloons have the warheads is how intense the beam must be in order to have a sufficiently strong particle signal for detection. To produce particle beams for this discrimination technique will require an accelerator capable of achieving the neutral-beam energies and intensities necessary for detection. One study concluded that prototypes of this system being developed, using a 100 million electron volt beam of hydrogen atoms with 0.1–1.0 amperes of current, will be adequate for discrimination only at distances under 250 kilometers from the warheads and decoys.[1]

There are conceivable ways for the offense to develop particle sources

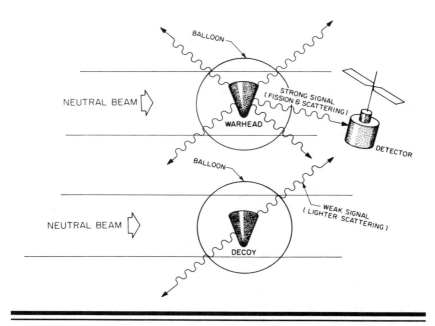

Fig. 4.1. Discrimination in the midcourse phase using neutral-particle beams to detect which balloons contain the real warheads. [Adapted from *SDI: Progress and Challenges, Pt. II,* staff report submitted to Senators William Proxmire and Bennett Johnston (March 1988)]

in the balloons that could simulate the warhead particle feedback, foiling the discrimination system, although this would be more difficult than using simple heaters to mask the infrared emission. Their effectiveness would depend upon how well the sources imitate the gamma-ray and neutron scattering from the warheads and how sensitive the defense detectors are to variations in the energy spectrum of the emissions in their discrimination.

There are three other general approaches that could be used in the effort to discriminate interactively which balloons have warheads. The first involves tapping the balloon to determine its vibrational modes by bouncing laser pulses off it. If the balloon has no warheads, the small force of the laser pulse gives the balloon a small push. If the balloon contains a warhead, then, when the balloon tries to move, it puts air pressure on the warhead (there will be a low pressure inside the balloon to keep it inflated). However, since the warhead is much heavier than the balloon, it will not move in response. The result is a recoil that acts back on the surface of the balloon, and a small vibration is set up in the balloon. This can be detected from the bounced laser signal. If the balloon had a decoy, there would be a slight difference between its observed vibration and that of a balloon with a warhead, although it appears unlikely that this difference could be detected.

There is an open question on whether the vibrations will even be adequate to tell any substantial difference between a balloon with a warhead and one without one. The strength of the recoil effect back on the balloon by the very small air pressure will be very slight because the warhead will not move. New optical instruments capable of detecting this minute difference have to be developed. Furthermore, there are other effects that could affect the small frequency shift measured in the return laser beam just as strongly as the warheads inside. Hitting meteoritic dust or small meteors by the balloons is one example, and several such impacts will occur. In addition, it is possible for the offense to use a type of tethering (tying together) of the warhead with the balloon that severely damps out any vibrations that would be set up in it. Thus, it is not clear whether this mechanism for detecting the warheads (particularly with effective tethering) will be viable.

A second approach to balloon discrimination involves deflections of the balloon. This would create a wobbling difference in the balloon response, depending or whether it has a warhead, a decoy, or nothing at all. An example of this would be to use small hypervelocity (high-speed) objects shot at the balloons. These would be shot from railguns that are designed to accelerate the objects to high speeds. These speeds would not have to be nearly as high as speeds necessary to destroy the balloon. The impact of these objects would set up a wobbling of the balloons about any objects they contain, and the nature of the wobbling would allow a distinction between balloons containing real warheads and those containing decoys. Balloons containing no central object would merely deflect.

The warheads and decoys could be tethered to the balloon to dampen this wobbling, and the creation of an effective damping device could probably be done easier than it could be done for vibrations. Thus it is more feasible to shield the balloon from this wobbling than it is to shield it from vibration. How effectively this could be done is undetermined at this point.

The third interactive discrimination method is actually to destroy the balloons to reveal any warheads inside of them. One way this could be done is to use hypervelocity objects of sufficient velocity to blow off or vaporize part of the surface of the balloon on impact. This could reveal the presence of the warhead inside it. Its use would require accurate tracking of the balloons. The accuracy of this technique is limited by the probable error in the determination of the location of the small balloon at the distances of separation by the tracking and by the probable error in the targeting. The balloon's location can be determined within 1 meter, but the error in targeting, which depends on the precision of the hypervelocity object launchers, may be larger.

If the error in hitting the balloon is only 0.001% (1 in 100,000), that puts the error at 10 meters for discrimination at 1,000 kilometers. An accuracy to within 0.001% is like shooting a bullet 1 kilometer (0.62 miles) away and hitting the target within 1 centimeter (0.39 inch). Thus hitting a small balloon with a hypervelocity object with this accuracy is about like hitting a bullet with a bullet nearly a mile away! The probability of hitting a balloon 1 meter wide is only about 1% for 0.001% accuracy. A defense with this accuracy would require 100 hypervelocity objects for every balloon it takes out.

Assuming a 95% boost-phase kill (which may never be achieved with all the potential countermeasures, such as the ones previously discussed and the ones to be introduced in Chapter 6), the 280,000 balloons that can be released in the midcourse will then be reduced to 14,000. If one hypervelocity object has an error of 0.0003%, it has about a 10% chance of hitting the balloon, so a minimum of 140,000 hypervelocity objects would be required. The midcourse part of the flight lasts almost 20 minutes, so it would be necessary to have destroyed the balloons within about 10 minutes to allow time for destroying the exposed warheads. Thus at least 240 hypervelocity objects will have to be launched per second. If the accuracy of the targeting is decreased to 0.001%, then 2,400 hypervelocity objects will need to be launched per second.

An open question is what mode will be used for the hypervelocity attacks. If the hypervelocity launches are made from satellites in orbit several hundred miles high, there will need to be several in orbit for every one that is covering the range where the targets can be. If they are being fired from the ground, they must be launched at the precise time necessary. Since the Soviets can launch their missiles in stages to exhaust the capabilities of the defense through the earlier-stage attacks or otherwise foil the defense in the case of a ground-launched attack, the orbital basing of the hypervelocity launchers may have the greater advantage.

On the other hand, by having the defense on satellites in predictable orbits, the offense can make an attack on the defense through a variety of means before the warheads come within range of the defense. The offense will know approximately where to strike the defense ahead of time (since the satellites lie in predictable orbits), while the defense has to determine the position of the warheads before it can attempt to strike them.

Another way proposed for destroying the balloons is to use a nuclear-pumped X-ray laser to "pop" the balloons (the X-ray laser is discussed in Chapter 3 and Appendix 6). The X-rays are absorbed in the thin surface of the balloon, and the balloon explodes. These X-ray lasers would be based on a submarine fleet, probably in the Atlantic Ocean, to be fired up when the missiles are in their midcourse. The X-ray lasers do not have the disadvantage for launching from the ground that the hypervelocity-object defense would, since the X-rays cover large sweeping areas. In contrast, the hypervelocity objects must be precisely targeted at each warhead. The 1987 American Physical Society study concluded the X-ray lasers may be viable discriminators if each X-ray laser has several independently targetable rods and if there are about as many X-ray lasers as there are missiles surviving the boost phase.

A similar nuclear-explosion technique is being investigated for the launching of hypervelocity objects. This is in a classified program through the Strategic Defense Initiative Organization (SDIO) called Project Prometheus. The purpose would be to channel the huge power of the initial blast of a nuclear explosion to launch hypervelocity objects in one direction. The blast would accelerate the objects to a very high velocity, causing them to escape before they could be devoured by the tremendous heat wave generated in the explosion. This technique is commonly referred to as a *nuclear shotgun*. Achieving the number and kinetic energy required for the hypervelocity objects would be easier than in conventional railguns and could more easily destroy the balloons and expose the warheads and decoys. It might also sufficiently damage the decoys to make it even easier for the defense to identify the warheads, unless the decoys are as hardened as the warheads are.

Midcourse Warhead Destruction

A method being developed to destroy the warheads after they have been exposed and their location determined is ramming kinetic-energy vehicles (high-speed objects that are larger and heavier than the hypervelocity objects) into them. The size of the kinetic-energy vehicles will range from that of a golf ball to a baseball and will be launched from railguns. The technique should be able to destroy the warheads in a head-on collision. It may not be possible to rely on the accuracy of the targeting and launching instruments in realistic battle conditions. The accuracy and the rapidity of the launches will determine the effectiveness of the defense.

The warheads are smaller than the balloons, generally less than a meter in length. Assume the total accuracy yields a 10% effective kill. If 1,000 warheads survive the boost phase (a boost-phase defense that is over 90% effective, which is likely not achievable with appropriate boost-phase countermeasures), then 10,000 high-speed objects will be needed. If the real warheads can be detected in the first 10 minutes of the midcourse phase, then 10 minutes are available for destroying the warheads. Thus a minimum of 16 kinetic-energy weapons will have to be launched every second.

In addition to the use of kinetic-energy kill projectiles, homing rockets are a possible candidate for destroying the warheads. One of the purposes of the Homing Overlay experiment and later Delta tests was the development of a possible midcourse ABM defense, as well as anti-satellite-capability development. (The close connection of antisatellite weapons with defense weapons is discussed in more detail in Chapter 8.) The proposal at the time of the Homing Overlay experiment was to have 1,000 launchers with three interceptors for each launcher, for a total of 3,000 interceptors to be used in the defense.[2]

If one assumes that 1,000 warheads survive the boost phase (again, an over 90% effective boost-phase defense) and a 50% likelihood of destruction of the warheads with homing rockets (probably the best that can be achieved in realistic battle conditions), a minimum of about 2,000 homing rockets will be required to destroy the warheads. If the boost-phase defense is only 75% effective, the minimum number of homing rockets with a 50% destruction rises to 6,000. With an expansion of the number of ballistic missiles deployed, the number of homing rockets and launchers must similarly be expanded. The Exoatmospheric Reentry Interceptor System (ERIS) is a homing-rocket system under development for phased deployment of a strategic defense (discussed in Chapter 7).

Counterattacks on a Midcourse Defense

The midcourse phase of a missile launch probably will become a battle if a midcourse defense is deployed to counter the warheads. This will occur because the same methods that the defense can use to attack the missiles can also be used by the offense to attack the defense. Furthermore, there are three advantages an attack on the defense has over the attack by the defense. The first is timing: The offense will undoubtedly know ahead of time where critical components, such as the launchers and the surveillance and tracking satellites, are before this phase is reached. Space-based systems on satellites lie on orbits that are easily determined and known ahead of time. Thus the offense can begin part of the attack on the midcourse defense before the missiles reach a midcourse phase (or even before the missile launch), while the defense must track, discriminate or expose, and target the warheads in the limited time available in the midcourse phase of the missiles.

The second advantage is that there are a number of sensitive critical systems on the defense. Warheads, on the other hand, are hardened objects that are set on their course, and the only critical system they contain is the mechanism to activate the nuclear detonation when it reaches its destination. On a defense there are optical and infrared systems for surveillance and tracking, computer hardware systems for battle management, systems to determine which warheads have not been destroyed and need retargeting, and so on. Each of these systems plays an integral part in the defense, and if any one of these is taken out, the effectiveness of the defense is significantly lowered if not removed.

The third advantage is that the requirements for the effectiveness of the attack on the defense are not as stringent. If the attack on the defense causes enough damage to one or more systems to reduce its effective kill to 50% of what it would otherwise be, then twice as many warheads survive to the next phase. The midcourse defense capability will have been considerably reduced. On the other hand, the defense needs to destroy 90% or more of the warheads to significantly ease the burden for the short terminal-phase defense. A 50% reduction in the capability of the defense is very effective, while a 50% destruction of the warheads is rather ineffective for the defense.

The nuclear-explosion methods for exposing the warhead, the X-ray laser and the nuclear shotgun, are also important possible methods for the Soviets to use to attack the defense if they can develop operational and effective X-ray-laser or nuclear-shotgun systems. If the Soviets could deploy their own X-ray-laser or nuclear-shotgun systems, they might be able to protect their warheads through a strategic placement of submarines with these weapons in positions below the path of the warheads. Since the submarine commanders of the offense will know of the positions and timing of the midcourse in advance, they can fire their laser rockets at the time appropriate to fire at and destroy U.S. ground-based defense rockets the moment they leave the atmosphere to counter the warheads. They may even use a staged attack by the offensive missiles to help outfox the defense in conjunction with attacks on the defense.

The X-ray laser or nuclear shotgun may similarly be used to counter sensitive space-based components of the defense used for surveillance, tracking, and discrimination. Taking out one of these systems will render the defense ineffective. The tracking and discrimination systems could likewise be countered by well-placed ordinary nuclear explosions. The offense can also attack space-based components of the defense by using a kinetic-vehicle system similar to that discussed for the defense to destroy the warheads.

There is a potentially effective counter to homing rockets used for a midcourse defense. This is a case where decoys will be very useful. The more decoys, the better, since they will make the homing rockets as likely to focus on the destruction of a decoy as a real warhead. Although methods for discriminating between decoys and real warheads can be partially effective, it is always possible to install enough decoys to overwhelm the system.

The economics of the use of decoys is an important factor. An early cost estimate by SDIO for a midcourse defense with 1,000 launchers and 3,000 interceptors was about $50 billion. But this midcourse defense could not possibly be adequate unless a more expensive boost-phase defense has already destroyed 90% of the missiles, leaving no more than 1,000 to 1,500 warheads by the beginning of the midcourse phase. Many decoys can be deployed in the midcourse at much lower costs than the warheads.

Assume, for example, that 4 times as many decoys were deployed as warheads and that a reasonably effective decoy discrimination system could identify 75% of the decoys. Then the number of interceptors necessary in the midcourse defense will have to be doubled to target both unidentified decoys and warheads in order to ensure that most of the warheads have been countered, increasing the defense cost to $100 billion. However, the cost of the 4,000–6,000 decoys (probably under $5 billion) would be considerably less than the $50 billion in extra defense required, providing a strong incentive to use decoys with an offense when a strategic defense is deployed.

Thus the cost of adding decoys is much lower than the cost of countering the decoys not positively identified by the defense. In fact, two factors — the very limited ability to estimate the number of decoys that will be used and the much lower cost of a decoy buildup — virtually guarantee that the offense can overwhelm a homing-rocket midcourse defense. (The implications of a trade-off between defensive versus offensive weapons costs are reviewed in more detail in Chapter 8.)

Terminal Defense

During the terminal phase, the time available to kill the warheads is, as in the boost phase, very short. The warheads come down and reenter the atmosphere at a high rate of speed, and a defense must be able to act quickly to have a chance of taking them out. Homing rockets and ground-based lasers are being developed for potential use in such a defense. Because of atmospheric propagation effects, which would be considerably worsened by nuclear explosions, homing rockets will have a greater advantage. The homing rocket High Endoatmospheric Defense Interceptor (HEDI) is being developed for a terminal-phase defense in the planned early deployment (discussed in Chapter 7).

The warheads reach the high terminal phase (atmospheric reentry, about 75 miles high) about 120 seconds before detonation. The balloons burn up at this point. The defense can attack the missile at this height, although it will be more difficult here than at lower heights, particularly because decoys are still present. They reach the low terminal phase about 50 seconds before detonation, at a height of about 20 miles. At this height all other decoys burn up. This point is the optimum one for attack on the warheads, but the time available to destroy them is quite short.

The defense will use an airborne tracking system in the terminal phase. The system being developed for this purpose by the SDIO is the Airborne Optical Adjunct (AOA), which detects infrared signals from the warheads and decoys. The reentry into the atmosphere generates significant heat, which radiates in the infrared. This infrared tracking will be supplemented with ground-based radar.[3]

A countermeasure can be used at this phase that can be effective in ensuring the survivability of many of the warheads while they are still at a very high altitude. This technique is known as *salvage fusing,* whereby some of the warheads descending torward a given target area are set to explode prematurely.

Salvage fusing can be done in two ways. Some of the first warheads can be set to explode automatically at very high altitudes (before they are in optimum range of the defense), and the rest of the warheads are brought in behind the explosion. Alternatively, some of the warheads can be triggered to explode automatically at the instant of an interception by the defense. In either case, the effect of the premature explosions of the salvage-fused missiles is to disrupt the ability of the defense to track the warheads behind the fireball for several seconds. The radiation from the explosion ionizes the surrounding atmosphere and is accompanied by a heat wave and considerable turbulence. (Ionization involves breaking up atoms and molecules into positive and negative charges.)

The explosion thus creates a plasma (an ionized gas), and none of the electromagnetic waves (such as radio waves and radar) can propagate in it unless they are of very high frequency. This phenomenon is analogous to a feature of the ionosphere (also a plasma)—shortwave radio signals cannot penetrate it and bounce off, providing long distance communication. On the other hand, television signals are higher frequency and penetrate the ionosphere, and hence are short-range unless the signals are relayed by satellite or cable.

For nuclear bursts at altitudes of around 40 miles or above, the beta particles (free electrons) from the explosion become trapped on the Earth's magnetic-field lines and can travel long distances. The beta particles and gamma rays from the nuclear explosion ionize the denser atmosphere below it and can produce a long-term blackout to the ground-based radar signals used in the tracking.[4] If the defense cannot determine where the warheads are, they survive until they reach lower altitudes.

For nuclear explosions from warheads that penetrate down to 10 miles altitude, the plasma density in the fireball is initially so high that none of the infrared or radar waves can penetrate it. After a few seconds this plasma density has dropped down sufficiently low to allow penetration. However, the damping and refraction (bending) of these waves created by particle collision and turbulence for explosions is so great in the immediate vicinity for the next minute or more that tracking capability is doubtful because of the large errors that result.

The lower-altitude nuclear explosions will cause destruction at the ground level, as well as major atmospheric turbulence. The atmospheric turbulence will create significant errors in tracking and targeting. Another countermeasure using the nuclear blasts is called *laddering*. In this scheme the first nuclear weapons come in and explode at high altitudes, and warheads successively come in behind these explosions to reach lower altitudes before they detonate (see Figure 4.2). The plasma produced in the vicinity of the fireball (which is longer-range at higher altitudes), will enable warheads behind the explosions to get to lower altitudes. Each nuclear explosion creates bubbles of plasma that help hide warheads.

An important point should be made about using this countermeasure. The warheads are hardened to withstand high temperatures in the reentry. Their design gives them some ability to survive in a nuclear explosion environment, but if they are too near a nuclear explosion when it occurs they can melt or disintegrate. The initial neutron radiation from the explosion will affect the unexploded warheads adversely, causing some fission which heats the warhead (although not the chain reaction created when the nuclear warhead itself explodes). The initial X-ray radiation from the explosion will affect unexploded warheads' casings. However, these will not seriously damage the warheads if they are sufficiently far from the explosion at the time of detonation. The neutron and X-ray radiation around the explosion drops rapidly in the few seconds after the explosion, so the warheads following the warhead that has exploded can be brought in shortly after the explosion. The huge shock wave of the explosion can

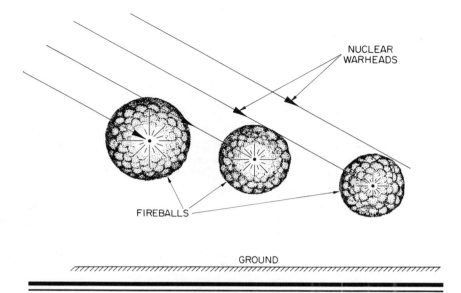

Fig. 4.2. The laddering countermeasure, using a sequence of nuclear explosions to blind the defense in the terminal phase.

certainly scatter the warheads but normally will not seriously damage them.

The AOA tracking system for locating the warheads has infrared (higher-frequency) detectors that are not blacked out except for low-altitude nuclear explosions. However, the major disruptions and interference due to the very turbulent nuclear explosion environment will be greatest for these higher-frequency waves. The reason is that higher frequencies correspond to shorter wavelengths, while in the explosion the very turbulent atmospheric waves and oscillations generated are dominant at these shorter wavelengths. This process will cause substantial random scattering of the infrared waves that the defense is trying to use to locate warheads in the nuclear-explosion environment, so they will be subject to large errors. Thus laddering can still be effective, even with those detectors.

There is another phenomenon that makes nuclear explosions an effective means of disrupting the communication that would be necessary for the defense to detect the warheads: *electromagnetic pulse*. When a nuclear explosion occurs, it creates a very intense broad band of wave frequencies that includes the radio range. The energy from these waves can cause much damage to sensitive electronic components associated with the defense unless they are adequately shielded, and it can be a major problem to the AOA infrared detectors and the radar receivers used to locate the warheads.[5]

The extremely high heat of the nuclear explosion creates intense infrared radiation which masks the infrared radiation coming from other warheads for a few seconds after the detonation. If the AOA receivers have sufficient sensitivity to locate the warheads, the electromagnetic pulse from the nuclear explosion could damage or destroy their capabilities. This sensitivity would naturally be greater for the later explosions that occur at lower altitude in the laddering scheme.

The pulse could damage the receiver enough to ruin its capabilities of effectively picking up accurate signatures of the warheads. Even if the receiver was sufficiently hardened so that no significant damage occurred, the intense noise that the receiver would be saturated with from the electromagnetic pulse would help mask the signatures of the reentry vehicles for a short time after the explosion. If laddering was used, there would be one explosion after another, each masking the signatures of the reentry vehicles. As the explosions come lower so that the warhead signatures are stronger, the intense noise from the pulse increases.

When the electromagnetic pulse of the nuclear explosion is combined with the turbulence created by the explosion disrupting the higher-frequency radio waves by rapidly scattering them, while plasma created by the explosion cuts off the lower-frequency radio waves, there appears in principle to be no way to get around well-devised laddering countermeasures.

There are other ways to lead the defense astray in the terminal phase. One would be to send in devices with the warheads that would simulate the radar signals that would be backscattered from a reentry vehicle during its radar detection. If this simulated radar signal was sufficiently intense, it could disguise the backscattered radar from the warheads, allowing for deep atmospheric penetration of the warheads. Utilizing effective techniques to fool warhead detection in the terminal phase will further decrease the effectiveness of a terminal defense.

CHAPTER 5

Requirements for a Defensive System

A ballistic-missile defense needs a number of fully automated subunits, all properly operating at the same time, in order to counter an offense. Two of these have been examined for proposed defensive schemes: the interceptor or kill mechanisms (directed-energy and kinetic-energy weapons) and discriminators to locate the true warheads. Several other requirements for a defense will be outlined.

Deployment Transportation

When a decision is made that the defense is ready to be deployed, the task of deploying hundreds or thousands of devices of substantial weight into space orbits will be a monumental job. Currently the space shuttle is used to transport satellites and devices for space-weapons experiments into space. The shuttle is adequate for the limited space transportation currently carried out, but the deployment of a space-based ballistic defense will be a much larger task.

The space shuttle transports satellites into orbit at an average cost of $5,000 per pound ($11,000 per kilogram). Estimates by SDIO for a strategic defense deployment involve launching as many as 5 million pounds into orbit per year.[1] This would cost $25 billion each year if the space shuttle was used for that purpose. Such a deployment would take several years, since 200 shuttle missions may be required for the first phase of the strategic defense.

The United States is developing the Advanced Launch System (ALS) for the purpose of transporting large and heavy loads into space to deploy

49

strategic defense weapons. This is projected to be completed by 1998, allowing deployment of the Phase I defense with the ALS to be completed by 2005. This assumes that a defense system has been constructed and a decision to deploy has been made by the time the ALS is ready. A goal for ALS development is to reduce the cost of the launching by a factor of 10. However, there is widespread skepticism that this can be achieved.

If the United States uses such a system to deploy a strategic defense that violates existing treaties (particularly the 1972 ABM Treaty, discussed in Chapter 10), and if no negotiations with the Soviets have been made to allow the launch, the Soviets would be motivated to interfere with the deployment. Antisatellite weapons and space mines could be used to damage or destroy partially deployed systems, preventing a complete system from being deployed. The length of time required in the deployment will be adequate for planning and deploying systems to counter the defense before its defensive capabilities have been completely activated.

Surveillance, Target Detection, and Tracking

In order for the defense to be alerted to a missile attack and have information on the location of the missiles or warheads for the period of their flight, the defense must be supported by a system of surveillance and tracking satellites. The defense alert in the boost phase must be made very quickly after the launch—within a few seconds, since the boost phase will end in 1 to 3 minutes. Every precious second taken before this alert of the defense takes away from the boost-phase time available to counter the missile, which is a critically short time. Continual satellite surveillance is necessary for detecting and tracking the missiles at the time of launching.

Surveillance and tracking satellites are vulnerable to an antisatellite (ASAT) attack. Furthermore, the Soviets will have deployed a number of advanced ASATs by the time the United States has deployed a ballistic-missile defense (motivating factors for this are discussed in Chapter 8). ASATs can be used to deny crucial information to the defense, creating significant uncertainty in the defense's ability to take out the bulk of the missiles. To aid their attack on our surveillance satellites, some antisatellite weapons could use nuclear explosives.

Currently the Boost-Phase Surveillance and Tracking System (BSTS) is being developed for the boost phase, and the Space-Based Surveillance and Tracking System (SSTS) is being developed for the midcourse. The BSTS will be based at high altitudes, beyond the range of current ASATs (but may be accessible from future ASAT development), making the initial detection (acquisition) and obtaining rough tracking data. This information is then communicated to the low-altitude interceptor, which homes in on the location obtained from the tracking data and targets the missile. The communication link between the BSTS and the interceptors can be countered (discussed in a later section).

With the future development of advanced ASAT systems, the Soviets may be capable of preceding an ICBM launch with complete ASAT attacks against the surveillance and tracking systems, which will severely limit the information available to transmit to the defense targeting system once the attack begins. Without all the necessary information as a result of partial destruction of the surveillance and tracking system or partial blockage of the communication relay to the interceptor, the defense ceases to be effective in targeting the missiles.

During the flight of the missiles in the boost phase and the warheads in later phases, several methods will be used for initial detection (acquisition) of each target, tracking them, and targeting them for destruction. During the boost phase, infrared sensors are used initially to locate the missiles. The heat given off by the rocket plumes has a very characteristic signature, so positive identification is generally reliable.

The accuracy of the determined location of the missile targets is limited by the inherent diffraction of the infrared waves as well as refraction by the atmosphere. For the infrared signals from the rocket plume the error in the location will typically be 0.1–1.0 kilometer. This will not be accurate enough for targeting the missile, since there is less than a 0.01% chance of hitting the target with this information. The information obtained from the targeting detection must be passed to a more accurate tracking system.

During the postboost and midcourse phases, radar and laser radar will be used for target detection (acquisition) and tracking. Laser radar (which uses optical rather than microwave frequencies) is needed to help discriminate individual warheads. However, these detection mechanisms have the difficulty that they can be "spoofed" or jammed. Spoofing can be done, for example, with the use of a cloud of aluminum chaff, which disrupts attempts to detect the target. Jamming can be accomplished by transmitting a large-amplitude, broad-frequency band of noise in the direction of the targeting vehicles. Target-detection mechanisms must be prepared to operate effectively under a variety of spoofing and jamming techniques, or many targets will remain undetected.

The tracking systems (as well as separate target-aiming systems, discussed in the next section) for the defense require very finely tuned, highly accurate optics. The sensitive optics required will be an Achilles heel for the defense, vulnerable to an attack by the offense. Furthermore, if the offense succeeds in seriously damaging the optical system, the defense will be blinded and thus rendered ineffective.

An effective approach for an ASAT attack on the defense would be to concentrate on the optics, since that is likely the most vulnerable system on the defense. The offense could counterattack the optical system on the defense by smaller-powered lasers. The optics on the defense will necessarily be amplifying the magnitude of remote light sources of the missiles in order to detect them clearly. Thus, if the offense counters with powerful lasers, amplification by the optical tracking system could produce signals so intense that they would cause major damage to the system. Even if such lasers do not seriously damage the optics, they could effectively blind the tracking and aiming systems, since then the discrimination of the much weaker optical signals of the targets is significantly more difficult. The defense would be rendered ineffective.

After reentry, the warheads heat up again and emit infrared radiation. Thus radar and infrared detectors can be used to detect the targets. A system that is being developed for this use is the Airborne Optical Adjunct (AOA), which would be airborne to detect the warheads high in the atmosphere at the start of the terminal phase of their trajectory. Since the infrared detectors have a limited accuracy, the information would be passed to a ground-based imaging radar for the tracking.

At the atmospheric heights at which the infrared detectors first detect the targets, it may not be possible to distinguish between real warheads and decoys. Thus the radar unit will need to gather tracking information on all the objects. All objects will have to be tracked until the decoys clearly separate from the true warheads at about 20 miles' altitude. Sufficient numbers of decoys reaching the terminal phase could overwhelm the tracking unit. Furthermore, as discussed in some detail in the last chapter, the radar can be rendered ineffective by blackout from nuclear explosions (in the salvage-fusing and laddering schemes). It also can be jammed by a broad-frequency band of noise from decoy emitters that survive the midcourse.

Targeting Systems

Once a target has been located and tracked by the defense, the directed or kinetic-energy weapon that is to destroy it must be accurately aimed. There are two inherent difficulties that must be dealt with in these tasks: the delay time created by the separation of the target and the defense weapon, and the inherent jitters in a space-based defense. (Homing rockets are a probable exception: These difficulties are more pronounced for weapons without in-flight corrections, such as lasers and kinetic-energy projectiles.)

Time delay occurs because the light or infrared waves propagate between the target and the defense in a finite time. Thus the target is seen to be in a position a few thousandths or even hundredths of a second after it is actually at that position. In that fraction of a second the fast-moving target will have moved tens or hundreds of meters. Furthermore, the target will have moved farther by at least the same distance once the defense fires at the target and the beam or kinetic-energy weapon has arrived back at the target. For the case of kinetic-energy pellets, this delay would be substantially larger, since it may take seconds for them to reach the target.

The total time delay must be precisely corrected to be able to hit the target, and that correction requires a determination of the distance of the target from the defense, the speed and direction of the target from the tracking data, and a simultaneous on-the-spot computation of this correction. If small auxiliary rocket engines capable of making rapid unpredictable small changes in the missile or warhead paths are installed, they can create significant errors in the tracking time-delay corrections, minimizing the defense's chances of hitting the target.

Jitters are inherent in any system based in space and can significantly affect the tracking and aiming tasks, limiting the accuracy of the process. Jitters arise because a space-based system is not based on a firm foundation as a system based on the ground would be, so it is difficult to stabilize the system against major vibrations that naturally arise in any system with moving mechanical units. The source of these vibrations arises from Newton's third law of motion: For every action (force) there is an equal reaction. If a system is on a firm ground-based foundation, most of the force reactions can be dissipated in the ground, so the force of the ground foundation balances the reaction force. This keeps the ground-based system from moving, as opposed to active space-based systems.

Consider, for example, the rapid swings in space-based bulk laser systems used to target the missiles in the boost phase. Upon each retargeting that occurs every few fractions of a second, a reactive rotating motion of the space platform that the laser is mounted on would have to be avoided. This can be partially countered with appropriate use of gyroscopes, but there will still be important vibrations left. Given the very high accuracy that will be required of the lasers, these vibrations will be a significant problem for accurate targeting.

The accuracy of target destruction is limited by the intrinsic diffraction of the (light) waves used in the tracking, the accuracy of time-delay determinations, jitters inherent in the targeting, and the precision of the targeting system. Since the defense will be hundreds of kilometers from the target, even an error of 0.001% (1 in 100,000) will be about 10 meters. With adequate countermeasures to increase the error, it may not be possible to achieve this accuracy.

Comparing the cross-sectional area of the target to the area of a circle with a radius equal to the probable error, one obtains the probability that the beam from the defense will intercept the target. At a distance of 1,000 kilometers (625 miles), the chances of hitting the target for a 0.001% targeting error will be about 1% for a warhead in the midcourse, somewhere around 10% for a missile in the boost phase. The defense will most likely miss the target the first time it fires. These accuracies would multiply the number of defense weapons and power needed in the defense for these stages by a factor of 10–100 from that determined from 100% accuracy.

Power Sources

Defense systems will require sources of sizable power to operate and function adequately. Power sources of 100 megawatts will be needed for each platform with chemical and free-electron laser and particle-beam weapons. These sources are most likely to be nuclear reactors. Large power sources will also be needed for kinetic-energy vehicles used in a defense. Currently the United States is developing the space nuclear reactor SP-100, which will operate at 100 kilowatts.

A report released in January 1989 by the National Academy of Sciences (a study requested by the Pentagon) stated that current space power sources are grossly inadequate for requirements of a strategic defense. The panel making the study was chaired by Joseph Gaven, Jr., who stated that meeting the requirements would necessitate substantial advances in power technology. Development of the power hardware should be given a higher priority in SDI, or the requirements will not be achieved. Space nuclear-reactor power systems like the SP-100 under development have too much weight for operation in space, and future technology will be needed to resolve this.[2]

The use of nuclear-reactor power sources on spacecraft has received criticism from the Federation of American Scientists. Daniel Hirsch has constructed a proposal with a group of Soviet physicists to prevent putting nuclear reactors in orbit. The Soviets have been using nuclear reactors as energy sources in spacecraft for years, and this has created problems, including a downed spacecraft that spread radioactivity over part of northern Canada. Hirsch stated that a ban must be put on nuclear reactors in orbit now, or perhaps hundreds of reactors would be in space in the next century. Given the fact that satellites in low Earth orbit slowly degrade because of small atmospheric pressures, this could become a major problem in the future.[3]

Intercept Confirmation

Because of potential errors in detecting, tracking, and targeting offensive weapons, the defense is very likely to miss the target on the first shot. This means that the defense must have a system for confirming the intercept, determining if the target is sufficiently damaged, and retargeting if the target has not been rendered inoperative.

It takes time for the course deviation of a missile or warhead to be evident, so the target will have to be tracked a number of seconds after firing at it. Since the defense station cannot wait for confirmation of each hit before targeting the next object, this confirmation will have to be done by a separate system simultaneously with the process of firing at other targets. (The BSTS and SSTS under current development will be assigned those tasks for the boost phase and midcourse.) Because the time over which the objects already fired at will have to be tracked considerably overlaps the time for firing and targeting a new target, the intercept-confirmation system must confirm many different intercepts simultaneously. Then, if an intercept is not confirmed or disconfirmed, the confirmation system will have to coordinate with the interceptor for retargeting.

A problem arises toward the end of the boost or midcourse phase if the particular defense for that phase is not useful in the next phase. The time needed for confirmation is much longer than the time needed for interception, so there will be inadequate time to confirm and retarget the targets that the interceptor has fired at late in the phase. Thus, many or most of the targets on which interception is attempted late in the phase will not be taken out, since there is insufficient time to retarget.

The intercept-confirmation system (like other defensive systems) must run autonomously and requires complete artificial intelligence capabilities for making decisions on retargeting. This means a very large amount of error-free computer software must be developed for this system to make accurate decisions on whether the intercept was successful. Developing the system requires extensive testing of that software under realistic conditions (discussed in a later section of this chapter). Anything approaching adequate testing to prepare for realistic battle conditions may not be feasible.

Command, Control, and Communication

In any military battle operation four things are essential: command, control, communication, and intelligence (often referred to as C^3I). Intelligence would be provided by the surveillance, target detection, tracking, and intercept-confirmation systems for the missiles or warheads. Other systems are needed to take care of the rest of the essentials (the C^3). These systems would have the task of coordinating each part of the defense. Effective communication among the sensors and the separate battle stations, as well as communication of the situation with ground-based monitoring stations, will be essential. Hence a complex communication network will be required.

An important point is that communication between the defense systems can be jammed by a broad-band emitter of waves of sufficient power that covers the frequency at which the defense communication is taking place. Effective jamming would prevent the defense systems from knowing what the others are doing; hence each defense would act independently of the others. This could create a situation where several defense systems are attacking the same targets, whereas other targets are not being attacked. Thus effective jamming would seriously decrease the effectiveness of the defense since the defense is incapable of assuring destruction of many of the targets.

Command and control systems are the brain and nerve center for the defense. These systems can be structured either so that they are highly centralized or so that they are decentralized, with various stations having a degree of autonomous control.

A centralized command and control structure would make all decisions for the defense, which would require intelligence gathering and communication with all parts of the defense. In that case communication disruption could hinder the effectiveness of the coordination, and successful attacks on the command and control systems could render the defense useless unless they are adequately shielded against the attack.

For a decentralized defense, a potential weakness is an ineffective coordination between all parts of the defense. Coordination between different parts of defense will be necessary to avoid a duplication in countering part of the offense and insufficient countering of other parts of the offense, and will require communication between the defense satellites and the tracking systems. Communication disruption could interfere with this coordination. Furthermore, effective discrimination between the warheads and decoys to determine the real targets will require the processing of data from several sensors. Having decentralized command and control will decrease the effectiveness of this discrimination.

The first-phase architecture studies for SDI, released in 1985, planned a tightly coordinated defense system with a highly centralized command and control. These studies planned an extensive defense with several layers based on thousands of satellites. These plans were discarded because such systems would be highly vulnerable to an attack and are generally unrealistic. Later architectures were constructed based on a more decentralized command and control. These were replaced with Phase I architectural studies when the SDIO refocused its effort on early deployment in 1987 (see Chapter 7).[4]

Battle Management and Software

The problem of providing total management for the battle between the missiles or warheads and the defense will be very complicated. In order to have a workable defense, technologies must be developed that allow implementation of a highly responsive, reliable, survivable, endurable, and cost-effective battle-management system. This will require an incredibly large amount of software that must all work in unison without flaws or "bugs." Computer software will need to be developed for aiming and controlling the sensors and weapons, for processing the high volume of data gathered from the sensors, for the surveillance to identify and track the targets, for decoy discrimination, for kill assessment and retargeting, for scheduling and allocation of weapons, for detecting counterattacks on the defense systems, and for dynamic reconfiguration to compensate for damaged components. In addition, it must be able to coordinate all components of the systems involved in the defense processes.[5]

The Fletcher Commission study at the outset of SDI estimated some 10 million lines or more of code will be needed, calling the task of developing, testing, and maintaining the software "a task that far exceeds in complexity and difficulty any that has yet been accomplished in the production of civil or military software systems." (Some estimates put the number of lines of code needed much larger.) The software code needed is much larger than software codes used in large mainframe computers today, which generally are a few hundred thousand lines long. Mainframe computer codes are developed over several years by many programmers through constant testing, debugging, and retesting.

The difficulty of writing complex interconnected computer codes increases much faster than the number of lines needed for the code. An estimate for the number of man-years needed for such a task is as high as 82,000.[6] The task of writing all of the code would require, for example, an organized group of 8,000 people engaged full-time for 10 years, and all parts of the code-development would have to be perfectly coordinated to allow for a consistent code to be written (see Table 5.1).

Table 5.1. Software requirements for mainframe computer versus battle management

	Mainframe Computer	Defense Battle Management
Lines of code	500,000	10,000,000
Man-years		
High	2,500	81,700
Low	500	13,400

Source: Herbert Lin, "The Development of Software for Ballistic Missile Defense," *Scientific American* 253 (December 1985): 46–53.

Note: The development tasks involve about 8% planning, 40% designing, 14% installing, and 38% testing and debugging.

No one can project the job involved for the complex codes that a strategic defense will entail. Computers will have to be developed that have the capability of generating their own software in order to write all of this code. According to the original report soliciting research proposals from universities made by the SDIO, software and hardware that have performance capabilities orders of magnitude beyond that of currently available technology will be needed.[7] This includes the development of processing speeds many orders of magnitude faster than any present-day computers and radically different architectures.

The SDIO report stated that nothing short of a major revolution in computer technology and software engineering can achieve these requirements. The computers involved will be at least sixth generation or beyond. The best computers available today are fourth generation, and current goals in the United States and Japan are to develop a fifth-generation system by the year 2000.

There are two problems inherent in the battle-management systems for the defense. The first is that the enormous amount of software needed can never be tested together. A large number of the bugs in the code could not be found and corrected until testing had been carried out many times under realistic nuclear war conditions. Some of the testing could be done on computer simulations of a nuclear war, but it would be impossible to carry out all the testing that would be required for a realistic nuclear battle. There are too many possible scenarios to build simulation models for testing, and some scenarios are unpredictable. One would have very low confidence in the full battle-management system.

In addition, the code must be written with guesses of the possible countermeasures that will be used. If the Soviets come up with countermeasures that have not been anticipated with an adequate response written in the code, the countermeasure could go unnoticed, and the offense would not be adequately countered by the defense. Since the number of countermeasures that can be invented and instituted are immense, this will almost certainly be the case. Thus we would have a low confidence in the ability of all the systems to work together properly and provide an adequate defense.

The second problem in the battle-management systems is that the decision to counter an attack must be made autonomously. There would be no time for relaying this information to the ground for military personnel to make that decision. Considering the low confidence level that we can place in it because of lack of complete testing, this prospect is frightening. For example, the defense might mistake the launch of civilian Soviet spacecraft for a missile attack and proceed to destroy them. These serious pitfalls make such weapons undesirable and potential contributors to an unstable military environment.

These and other problems were underscored in 1985 by Dr. David Parnas, who served on the SDIO Panel on Computing in Support of Battle Management. Dr. Parnas is a chaired professor at the University of Victoria, British Columbia, a principal consultant for the Software Cost Reduction Project at the Naval Research Laboratory in Washington, D.C., and has taught at several other universities. His expertise and interests include programming semantics, language design, program organization, process structure and synchronization, and precise abstract specifications.

Dr. Parnas resigned from the panel and submitted several short essays on the fundamental problems of developing the software required with battle management. Questions he addresses in these include why software in general is unreliable (i.e., has a fundamentally different character from hardware, machines, devices, etc.), why it will be particularly untrustworthy on SDI systems, and the limits of software capability. Included in his analysis are discussions of the reasons that artificial intelligence, automatic programming, and program verification cannot improve this problem or make the software reliable.

He also pointed out that even if the required software could be developed, since we do not know all the techniques the Soviets will use, we could never know how long it would take do all the analyses and processing that would be required of this software. It may take a second, which is an allowable time; it could take a minute, which debilitates or nullifies the boost-phase defense; it could take half an hour, in which case the defense is useless.

Three of Dr. Parnas's conclusions are noteworthy. The first is that we can have no confidence in a system under these circumstances, so that nuclear weapons are still a potent threat. The second: "I am not a modest man. I believe that I have as sound and broad an understanding of the problems of software engineering as anyone that I know. If you gave me the job of building the system, and all the resources that I wanted, I could not do it. I don't expect the next 20 years of research to change that fact." The final one: "There is no justification for continuing with the pretense that the SDI battle-management software can be built just to obtain funding for otherwise worthwhile programs. DOD's overall approach to research management requires a thorough evaluation and review by people outside of DOD."[8]

If this evaluation is correct, it means an effective strategic defense cannot be developed in any meaningful technological sense, since without the required software, all of the hardware is useless. The possibility of developing reliable software with the nonexistence of realistic testing is vanishingly small. Even if the software needed for a defense system can be developed, we will never know whether it will work reliably until it is given the real test: a nuclear attack on the United States. On the other hand, the focus the SDI program has placed on the development of new technologies in computer software and hardware will have more reliable applications to other (offensive) weapon systems.

Note added in proof: Information has been leaked on a classified nuclear rocket propulsion program in SDI code-named Timberwind. The propulsion system would use tiny nuclear-reactor fuel elements to provide an environment of 5000°F temperatures through which liquid hydrogen would be pumped. The very rapid expansion of the liquid hydrogen into hot gas would blast out the rocket nozzle, providing 2–3 times the thrust of standard rocket engines.*

The concept was originally proposed to support the launch of directed-energy weapons, such as the X-ray laser, on demand. In 1990 the Defense Science Board Task Force on SDIO Advanced Technology endorsed the concept. In a related program a nuclear-powered rocket engine is being developed for transporting heavy loads into space. In this use the engine would replace stages of an Atlas or Titan rocket. The reactor would operate near the fuel melting point for maximum efficiency. Using it for stages within the atmosphere would be a clear violation of nuclear safety standards, and even its use outside the atmosphere would still pose a low probability of it releasing radioactivity into the environment.**

An unsatisfactory ground test of this was performed at Sandia National Laboratory in the late 1980s. A suborbital (basically atmospheric) flight test over waters near Antarctica has been proposed. Such a test would carry a small risk of crashing near populated regions.

---

*"Star Wars Does It Again," *Time*, April 15, 1991, 36.
**"Star Wars Nuclear Rocket Program Disclosure," Federation of American Scientists, April 1991.

CHAPTER 6

Countermeasures

One of the biggest difficulties that defensive systems face is the number of lower-cost countermeasures that the offense can take against them. Several have been introduced, and several more are available for use. Some of these were analyzed in anti–ballistic missile discussions in the sixties and are just as effective today.[1] An overview will be made of the main countermeasures that are relatively inexpensive compared to the costs of the defensive systems. In principle, others can be developed that are useful and affordable.

Decoys

Decoys can be launched with the missiles in the boost phase, as well as released in the MIRVing of the missiles after the boost phase ends. Their cost is much smaller than that of armed missiles, and they can be used to increase the number of targets the defense must discriminate or destroy. In the boost phase accurate sensors can discriminate between the plume of a decoy and a real missile, but it will be more difficult to detect decoys in the midcourse phase and the first part of the terminal phases.

In the boost phase decoys can be effectively hidden by introducing well-designed "antisimulation" devices to alter the steady flight of the real missiles. The missiles have well-developed inertial guidance systems leading to a very smooth flight, while the decoys would have detectable "staggering" without those systems. Antisimulation devices introduce a fake staggering of the missiles, making them move as the decoys do. Inability to discriminate the decoys from the missiles would require the targeting and destruction of all launched vehicles. On the other hand, if the defense is designed to ignore targets it identifies as decoys, it could ignore some of the real missiles.[2]

As discussed in Chapter 4, the defense can release tens of thousands of balloons (e.g., ones with an aluminum surface) in the postboost phase along with the warheads and decoys. The balloons can be used to hide the warheads and the decoys, and many of the balloons will be left empty. The defense must destroy the balloons or differentiate which contain the real warheads, by either examining the residual heat left from the boost phase or examining their response to interactive discrimination with lasers or neutral beams.

The discrimination with the infrared emissions from the residual heat is probably not reliable because the infrared emission from the Earth is about as large. Furthermore, heaters can be used with the decoys to simulate the low infrared emissions of the real warheads. Similarly, a particle emitter can be used to camouflage the particle emissions of a real warhead when the defense uses neutral beams to detect the actual warheads. Laser-beam discrimination can be countered by connecting the balloons from each warhead and possibly by connecting each balloon to any warhead inside it. Effective countermeasures will make it very difficult and unreliable for the defense to try to detect the warheads without first destroying the balloons and then destroying every device that has characteristics similar to those of a warhead. If the Soviets are effective in disguising their decoys in this phase, then they will be able to overwhelm a midcourse defense with a proliferation of decoys.

In the terminal phase the decoys begin burning by the time they have descended to an altitude of about 20 miles. However, an effective terminal defense must first attack the warheads at high altitudes in the atmosphere (about 75 miles). In the high-altitude attack it must be able to discriminate between the emissions of decoys and warheads, or it must try to destroy all objects. The infrared signatures of the warheads and the decoys differ, and the Airborne Optical Adjunct (AOA) is currently being developed for discrimination and tracking. Countermeasures against decoy discrimination using high-altitude nuclear explosions were discussed in Chapter 4 and will be summarized in a later section.

Fast-Burn Boosters

The Soviets could deploy fast-burn boosters, such as those the United States used in the Sprint and Safeguard missiles, to lower the boost-phase time of their missiles to as short as 40–50 seconds. Times as long as 150 seconds would beat a submarine-launched X-ray-laser boost-phase defense because it will take longer for the defense rockets to reach the height needed to counter the missiles unless many millions of pounds of fuel are used in the defense rockets. Such fuel requirements make submarine launching for a boost-phase defense unfeasible.

In Appendix 13 a determination is made of how short the boost-phase times must be to end in the atmosphere. At the present launch angle of 23°, it requires shortening the boost-phase time to about 60 seconds to end the missile boost phase inside the atmosphere (below 100 kilometers' altitude). The Soviets can probably achieve a launch time as low as 50 seconds with fast-burn boosters in another decade. Since X-ray-laser beams (including a laser based in space), particle beams, and longer-wavelength chemical-laser beams are rapidly scattered and dispersed at 100 kilometers altitude in the atmosphere, this nullifies their effective usage as a defense in the boost phase. For a 50-second boost-phase time the boost phase would end about 80 kilometers in altitude, so the missiles would even avoid penetration of the upper part of the atmosphere the laser weapons might achieve by bleaching.

By developing a short boost phase that ends with the missile in the atmosphere, the Soviets could also make the missiles inaccessible to homing rockets in a boost-phase defense. For example, the homing rockets currently move only a maximum of 10 kilometers (6.25 miles) per second. To reach a target of 1,000 kilometers (625 miles) away, they would take over 100 seconds, longer than feasible boost-phase times.

Developing homing rockets faster than 10 kilometers per second would require an incredible increase in the fuel-tank size (see the fuel mass increase with terminal velocity for a homing rocket with a 100 kilogram payload in Table 6.1). Even if faster kinetic kill vehicles can be developed by using much larger fuel tanks, they still will run into major difficulties in countering missiles in the upper atmosphere because atmospheric effects will cause errors in the homing systems. The atmospheric friction on the homing rocket causes it to heat up and emit infrared radiation, which masks the radiation from the target plume. The use of decoy infrared-emitting devices by the offense would further counter any discrimination capability that the rocket might have.

The allowable time for ending the boost phase in the atmosphere could also be lengthened from 60 seconds by using lower ICBM trajecto-

Table 6.1. Homing rocket fuel mass required for a 100-kilogram payload

Terminal Velocity (kilometers/second)	Fuel Mass (kilograms)
10	2,803
15	14,841
20	78,577
25	416,026

Note: 1 kilogram = 2.2 pounds; 1 kilometer/second = 2,236 miles/hour

ries (see Figure 6.1). Present ICBM trajectories are determined by missiles rising off the surface of the Earth at an angle of 23°, chosen to minimize the amount of fuel used in its path from the Soviet Union to the United States. The angle can be raised or lowered, but at the expense of using larger fuel tanks and more fuel on the missiles. The Soviets may find it advantageous to change this angle if the US begins to deploy a missile defense. By lowering the angle to 15°, the missile spends 90 seconds in the atmosphere, allowing a 90-second boost-phase time still to end the boost phase in the atmosphere.

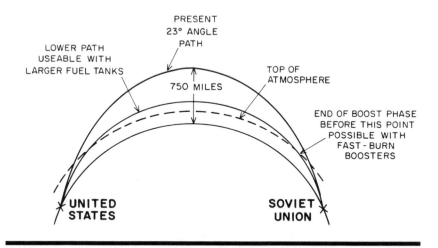

Fig. 6.1. Possible trajectories of an ICBM. The present minimum fuel trajectories of a 23° launch angle can be lowered if larger fuel tanks are put on the missile. By lowering the angle, the missile spends more of its boost-phase time in the atmosphere.

The boost-phase defense systems that can still be effective when fast-burn countermeasures are developed are shorter-wavelength chemical lasers and orbiting mirror systems using the excimer or free-electron lasers. However, since the boost-phase time will be considerably shortened by the fast-burn boosters, the boost-phase defense must be accordingly increased in size. Also, there are other countermeasures that could be effective against these systems, such as attacks on the geosynchronous mirror or orbiting mirrors in the mirror defense, and the low-orbiting platforms in the chemical-laser defense. Without a viable boost-phase defense it will be much more difficult to have an effective ballistic-missile defense.

Countering Target Detection and Tracking

Crucial to any defense is the ability to detect and track the target. As discussed in the last chapter, radar and laser radar used for detection and tracking, as well as essential communication between the systems for tracking and targeting, can be jammed with broadband signals. Higher-power lasers or transmitters can blind the sensors for detecting and tracking. The first section outlined ways of spoofing detection of infrared signatures by creating decoy signatures and disguising the actual missiles through antisimulation techniques.

Other countering techniques include surrounding the missiles by aluminum chaff or smoke clouds. Aluminum chaff can be particularly effective against radar because it causes random backscattering of radar waves. This degrades the radar reaching the targets and substantially interferes with target radar reflected back to the detector. Smoke clouds can effectively counter infrared detection since they absorb and scatter the infrared radiation created by the rocket plume, thus helping to hide the targets. If the smoke clouds were used along with decoy infrared devices, a homing-rocket defense would have a high failure rate.

The same screening devices can be useful in rendering laser and particle beams fired by the defense less potent. Aluminum chaff would have the effect of partially breaking up laser beams through multiple scattering and absorption on the aluminum sheets. The particulate matter in smoke clouds would similarly absorb and scatter energy from infrared laser beams used in a chemical laser defense. In the case of neutral beams used for a defense, the smoke and chaff would slow the beams through molecular collisions, decreasing their energy. These collisions would also cause ionization of some of the particles in the beam, whereupon the Earth's magnetic field would cause the particles to go astray of their target. Thus aluminum chaff and smoke screens not only serve the purpose of countering the detection of the missile but also help to shield the missiles from laser or particle beams.

Missile-Surface Shielding

The surfaces of the missiles can be coated to protect against laser beams. Ablative coating would be used—materials which have a high heat capacity and evaporate when heated. Evaporation absorbs much of the heat. A simple example is to cover the surface with a layer of water that is continually replenished. Since water has a very large heat capacity, it can undergo significant heating without a major change in temperature, helping to protect the missile from the effects of heat. As the water boils off much of the heat is taken with it.

The missile itself can be designed to produced a highly reflective surface, minimizing the amount of power that is actually absorbed by the missile for certain laser defenses. The focus on the design would be for reflectivity of the frequencies (infrared to ultraviolet) of the laser beams used in the defense. The surface can also be protected by a layer of a highly absorbing material such as asbestos. Asbestos burns at a very high temperature, so the laser will burn the asbestos more slowly, significantly increasing the time required to destroy the missile.

The above shielding techniques will not be effective against an X-ray-laser defense. In this case all of the energy of the X-ray beam gets absorbed in a very thin outer layer (about 0.1 of a micrometer), and the layer explodes. A possible way to protect a missile or warhead from the X-rays is to cover the surface with a shock-absorbing material (e.g., a foam) and place a false surface over that to absorb the X-rays. The X-rays will explode the outer layer, but the shock-absorbing material may shield the true missile surface adequately from the explosion so that it suffers little harm.

These techniques of shielding are by no means adequate to ensure that the missiles and warheads are unharmed. However, they have the effect of increasing the amount of power that the defense needs to deliver to the targets to destroy them by a factor of 10 to 100 (even more if cleverly designed).

Effective shielding of the missiles will necessitate the building of a much more powerful defense. However, the shielding techniques are simple to use and moderately inexpensive relative to the expense that will be required to increase the power levels of the defense some tenfold to a hundredfold. Thus missile shielding increases the cost of building an adequate strategic defense at a more modest cost to the offense.

Shielding is another example of the relative economics of defense versus that of offense: Given a race between the offense on one side and the defense on the other with equal monetary resources, the offense will win. This has important implications, discussed in the next section.

Buildup of Offensive Missiles

Another countermeasure to the defense would be to build up offensive boosters and warheads. As in the case of shielding of the missiles, there is similarly a larger cost for a country building more defensive stations compared to the cost of the extra offense installed by its opponent.

Take, for example, the boost-phase defense using chemical lasers in low Earth orbit. For every 1,000 missiles the Soviets add to their fleet, a minimum of another 300 defense satellites would need to be added to the defending fleet (the discussion in Appendix 5 shows it may be significantly larger). But this is a losing proposition because each new ICBM will cost around $25 million, whereas each new defense satellite will cost around $1 billion. The cost of the added offense is much less than that of the added defense by a factor of over 10! If we were engaged in an arms race with the Soviets by our buildup of strategic defense along with their expansion of offensive forces, the monetary trade-off would cause the United States eventually to lose the race.

A claim was made several years ago by certain proponents of strategic defense that the chemical-laser defense has a numerical advantage over an offensive buildup (shown to be invalid shortly thereafter). This claim was that as the Soviets increase their number of missiles by a factor of N (for example, N could be 4, corresponding to a quadrupling of their number of missiles), the United States has only to increase its number of defense satellites by $\sqrt{N}$ (which in the example would be 2, requiring us to only double our defensive forces).[3]

If this relationship were correct, with the monetary trade-off the cost of the defense to counter the new missiles that are being built would still not come down to the cost of those new missiles until the Soviets have increased their arsenal by about a factor of 100 from their present number! If the Soviets made an extremely massive buildup, by adding 1,400 new ICBMs every year, it would take 100 years to reach that point.

The relationship was shown not to be a correct one, for two reasons. First, it assumes the missiles are uniformly distributed inside the Soviet Union. The Soviets could concentrate their buildup into sufficiently small launch areas, and the size of the defense needed to counter it increases approximately in direct proportion to the increase in offensive forces. The second is that the relationship does not consider the time required to retarget the laser after it has been fired (i.e., it assumes the time to be 0).[4] That time causes an additional increase in the number of defense units required to counter the missiles (see Appendix 5). The defense remains more expensive than the offense regardless of the size of the offensive buildup.

In the case of the use of excimer or free-electron lasers used with geosynchronous and orbiting mirrors, the total costs include the cost of each power station and its fuel reserves, the cost of each orbiting mirror, the large cost for the geosynchronous mirror, as well as auxiliary systems for detection, tracking, and assessing. In Chapter 3 it was mentioned that the cost of fuel alone for each missile taken out, at present minimum costs for power generation, is estimated to be $150 million per missile countered. Thus the minimum fuel required to destroy a missile alone is currently about six times the cost for the missile, and the cost for the mirrors and other components of the defense will increase the unit cost considerably.

These costs only cover the boost-phase defense. In addition, the midcourse and terminal defense will have to be built up if the Soviets increase their offensive force. The cost of the midcourse and terminal defense will also increase proportionally for each missile that the Soviets add. Hence the cost advantages to the offense will be larger than the above estimates for the boost-phase costs.

It should also be noted that the Soviets can increase the cost of the defense over that of the offense by building up their offensive forces primarily with single-warhead missiles. The reason is that a sizable majority of the defense costs are for the boost-phase defense, and the number of warheads on a missile plays no role in requirements for the defense to take out each missile in the boost phase. By concentrating their buildup on single-warhead missiles, the Soviets can cut the cost of the missile by 50% or more, and the corresponding buildup of the boost-phase defenses will still be the same expense.

The economic advantages an offense-oriented country will have over the defense will be a strong incentive for the side with the offense to overwhelm the defense by a buildup. The building of a defense will not help stop the arms race (as claimed by some SDI proponents) but is likely to accelerate it. Furthermore, the defense poses potential offensive uses and threats, so the Soviets may believe that they have no choice but to proliferate their offensive forces (discussed in more detail in Chapter 8). This will provide further motivation for acceleration of the arms race.

Nuclear Explosions

Several countermeasures using nuclear explosions were introduced in Chapters 4 and 5. A high-altitude nuclear explosion while missiles are in the boost phase can counter effective missile tracking by blinding the infrared sensors as well as countering certain types of defense destructive mechanisms. The explosion increases the atmospheric pressure around it, sending some of the air in the upper atmosphere into the nearby space environment. The result is that neutral particle beams from boost-phase satellites accessible to the missiles are ionized and then scattered by very small atmospheric pressures, thereby being rendered ineffective (see Appendix 12).

Another important effect involves large-amplitude electromagnetic waves (radio or higher frequency) that are generated during the nuclear explosion (the electromagnetic pulse, or EMP, introduced in Chapter 4). The EMP will cause major interference with necessary communication links in the boost-phase defense, coordination between the defense stations, and intelligence necessary for retargeting. Communication is necessary between the systems used for surveillance and tracking, and the systems used for targeting. It is also required for coordination of defense satellites to avoid separate satellites attacking the same targets and leaving others untouched. Intelligence is necessary to determine if the targeting is successful in destroying the target. Thus the EMP from the explosion will allow some of the missiles or warheads to escape the defense.

Airborne optical systems will be used for early detection in the terminal phase, supplemented with ground-based radar systems for the tracking and targeting. The offense may be capable of blinding the infrared sensors of the defense used for discrimination by initiating a few high-altitude nuclear explosions. The infrared emissions of these detonations will be much more intense than the emissions from the warheads and decoys. In addition, they would create turbulence in the high-altitude atmosphere that could create substantial errors in tracking. The defense would not be able clearly to separate the warheads from the decoys until the decoys burn below 30 kilometers' altitude.

Salvage-fusing and laddering countermeasures in the terminal phase of the warheads were introduced in Chapter 4. Salvage fusing and laddering can render the ground-based tracking and targeting system unusable. These countermeasures counter ground-based detection and tracking through the cutoff of lower frequencies and induce strong scattering, particularly for higher frequencies.

Damage to the critical electronics of the terminal defense used in tracking and targeting may be caused by the EMP generated as a result of the nuclear explosions. This could counter both the ground-based and air-based systems unless all the electronics is soundly hardened. Future nuclear weapons that enhance the EMP may be used to damage the critical electronics even if it is adequately hardened for normal nuclear explosions (this is one type of the third-generation nuclear weapons discussed in Chapter 9).

Attacks on the Defense

Space-based systems are necessary for the boost-phase defense (in the exceptional case of submarine-based X-ray-laser rockets, the rockets cannot reach sufficient altitudes before the end of an anticipated boost phase unless they are so heavily loaded with fuel that they are too heavy to launch from submarines). Space-based systems will also be necessary for detection and tracking in the midcourse phase. These space-based systems are open to attack by antisatellite weapons (ASATs) by the offense. The Soviets could develop ASATs using homing rockets to attack the satellites from aerospace planes, similar to current U.S. ASATs, or from space-based satellites.

For a low-orbiting defense, an ASAT attack on the defense can be made prior to launching the missiles and the missiles launched after the defense has been crippled. As discussed in Chapter 4, the requirements on the attacking ASATs to effectively impair the defense are considerably less stringent than the requirements of the defense to destroy the missiles. Significantly impairing one critical system on the defense could render it ineffective or inoperative, allowing a sufficient number of missiles to get through. On the other hand, the defense must be able to destroy completely virtually all the attacks against it to ensure survival, or critical parts of the defense may be rendered inoperative.

Critical systems on the defense (introduced in Chapter 5) that are vulnerable to ASAT attack include the optical system used for detection and tracking, essential communication links between the defense stations, and computer hardware essential for command, control, and battle management. In addition, the finely aligned mirrors in a laser defense system, the finely aligned magnetic-field instruments in a particle accelerator, and the intricate homing devices on homing rockets are also vulnerable. Sophisticated high-technology systems are particularly vulnerable in the low Earth orbits used for a boost-phase defense.

A homing rocket can be nuclear tipped, so that a single rocket in an attack by the offense would significantly impair critical systems on several defense satellites rather than a single satellite. Thus the number of ASATs can be significantly lower than the number of defense satellites it attacks. Although the internal electronics and hardware may be sufficiently hardened to a nuclear detonation, major optical systems and communication links cannot.

Space-based ASATs could be widely separated or could be put close together in orbiting patches. Furthermore, decoy satellites can accompany the ASATs. This will prevent the defense from effectively destroying the ASAT systems by counterattacking unless accurate interactive discriminators succeed in determining the actual targets, or the defense is capable of destroying both the ASATs and the decoys.

Space mines could also be launched into orbits that would cross the orbits of the defense satellites, both in low orbit and geosynchronous orbit. They could be put into orbits to trail important defense satellites, and exploded when desired. For example, a signal could be sent to detonate them before launching the missiles, creating major impairment of the defense. The explosive device on the mines could be nuclear to ensure effectiveness.

If a geosynchronous mirror is placed into orbit for a mirror defense, it could be attacked with ground-launched rockets, possibly with nuclear warheads, designed to reach the mirror in its geosynchronous orbit. These could be used to severely damage or destroy the mirror by detonating in the vicinity of the mirror. The mirror will need to be finely aligned to be able to reflect a laser beam from a station 22,000 miles away down to orbiting mirrors also 22,000 miles away and will be very vulnerable to attack.

In addition to the use of a variety of ASATs to attack the defense, the Soviets could develop ground-based lasers for this purpose or even build laser systems to travel with their missiles for attacking the defense. Ground-based lasers could also be used to attack a defense launched from ground in the midcourse.

If the United States builds a missile defense, it will be a motivation for the Soviets to develop and build less expensive systems to attack the defense. With such an attack capability, they will determine the orbits of the defense satellites and continually track them, so they will know the positions at which to carry out the attack in a missile launch. Thus the attack on the defense will have significant advantages in surprise and timing.

It is possible to position a large fleet of defense satellites in orbit, but it will never be possible to put a sufficient number in orbit to provide confidence that the number will be sufficient to destroy the missiles in a major launch after a direct attack on the defense. Spending up to a trillion dollars to deploy such a fleet, while the Soviets could more cheaply deploy systems to attack the defense and render it ineffective, would be counterproductive and foolish.

CHAPTER 7

Phased Deployment of a Strategic Defense

The Strategic Defense Initiative was initially set out as a program to make "nuclear weapons impotent and obsolete," with the first phase to be a "research and technology" (research and development) program to determine whether a space defense is feasible. The new technologies that were being explored to make this conceivable through an effective boost-phase defense were laser and particle beams. Research under SDI has shown that these technologies are apparently decades away from attaining the requirements for deploying a missile defense.

However, the research on lasers and particle-beam weapons was substantially shifted in late 1986 and early 1987 to place a greater emphasis on kinetic-energy weapons. The shift occurred with the planning of an early deployment of a first-phase (Phase I) defense, composed entirely of layers of kinetic-energy weapons. Laser and particle-beam weapons would be deployed as later phases of the defense.

There are several reasons that motivated the shift to phased deployment. The research on directed-energy weapons was not producing rapid results to make a promising defensive system in the foreseeable future. Meanwhile, there was pressure from Congress to see what tangible results justified the rapid growth of the SDI budget. The shift was important for the U.S. commitment to a missile defense since it moved up the timing for initial deployment. The SDI program was being changed from a research and development program to one with greater emphasis on testing and construction. This was expected to produce more tangible results and make it more difficult to abandon the strategic defense program in the future, both of which help to cement the program politically.

The move to early deployment also changed our arms control commitments, pushing for the United States to break out of the 1972 ABM Treaty with preparations for Phase I deployment (discussed in Chapter 10).

The Shift of the Strategic Defense Initiative to Early Deployment

This shift was not a move sanctioned by Congress or even the president. There was a growing advocacy for early deployment among certain groups within the SDIO in the latter part of 1986 along with a shift in the funding in SDIO toward kinetic-energy weapons. This move was publicly endorsed by Secretary of Defense Weinberger in early 1987.[1]

The shift was intended to accelerate the development of kinetic-energy weapons because successful advances in their research made them more readily available. Plans were developed for a Phase I deployment of a defense with those devices in the early 1990s. Defenses built with directed-energy weapons would come along later to be used in successive phases of deployment. Secretary Weinberger stressed in his speech endorsing early deployment that a Phase I defense should defend populations, not just military bases, and would serve later as an integral part of a more comprehensive system of defense with directed-energy technologies.

Others in the Reagan administration were supportive of this move. For example, Attorney General Edwin Meese said the administration should deploy the first phase so it would "not be tampered with by future administrations." Proponents saw this move as a means of solidifying a strategic defense while President Reagan and his anticipated successor Vice-President George Bush were in office.[2]

The early-deployment shift received encouragement from Gen. Daniel Graham's High Frontier project, which planned a boost-phase defense against missiles using homing rockets in the early 1980s. Their proposal apparently did not have a strong influence on President Reagan when he proposed the Strategic Defense Initiative, since the early emphasis was on laser and particle-beam research and development for a boost-phase defense. However, High Frontier put out a proposal for early deployment in the fall of 1986 that consisted of three layers (boost, midcourse, and terminal defense) which would use kinetic-energy weapons for all three layers.

At about the same time as the High Frontier proposal, the Heritage Foundation put out a proposal that would only have a midcourse layer and a different terminal defense. Then the Marshall Institute put out a proposal later in the fall of 1986 with a three-layered defense with the boost- and midcourse-phase defense the same as the High Frontier proposal, but with a more sophisticated terminal defense. This proposed defense was adopted by SDIO in the early-deployment shift.[3]

Part of the motivation for early deployment came from the success the United States had in developing ASAT weapons with homing rockets, as well as successful tests of kinetic-energy weapons under SDI. For example, the successful Homing Overlay and Delta experiments (discussed in Chapter 3) made kinetic-energy weapons more attractive in the short term than directed-energy weapons. The Delta 180 experiment in September 1986 had demonstrated kinetic kill by the collision of two Delta rockets. These successes, along with pressures for results, were important factors in the shift toward planning for an early deployment using these systems.

The Phase I defense, initially planned for deployment in the 1990s, would consist of three layers for boost-phase, midcourse-phase, and terminal-phase defenses:[4]

1. Space-Based Interceptors (SBIs) (formerly known as Space-Based Kinetic Kill Vehicles, or SBKKVs). The boost-phase defense layer would use homing rockets launched from satellites in low Earth orbit to attack the missiles. The Boost-Phase Surveillance and Tracking System (BSTS) at high altitudes would be used for early warning and rough tracking data to transmit to the low-altitude interceptor for homing in on the precise location. There is an open question as to how soon the BSTS would be made sufficiently accurate in its determination of the rough tracking data to allow for the homing mechanism to take over after the transmission.

The SBI and the BSTS are also supposed to continue into missile postboost phase to attack the buses before the warheads, balloons, and decoys are released. However, the effectiveness of the BSTS in this phase is highly questionable. It would need to be much more sensitive to detect the postboost vehicles with the infrared detector after the missile plume is gone. The infrared emissions of the Earth mask these low-frequency and low-amplitude emissions and probably will nullify the use of the BSTS.

2. Exoatmospheric Reentry Vehicle Interceptor System (ERIS). The midcourse defense would use ground-launched rockets releasing kinetic-rocket (ERIS) interceptors to attack the warheads (see the diagram of the vehicle in Figure 7.1). The rockets would be launched from the United States. They would be accompanied by the Space-Based Surveillance and Tracking System (SSTS), which would relay data to the ground-based system. The SSTS systems would consist of 50–100 low-altitude satellites designed for tracking the postboost vehicles (still warm from boosting) and midcourse warheads (relatively cold) by using infrared detection

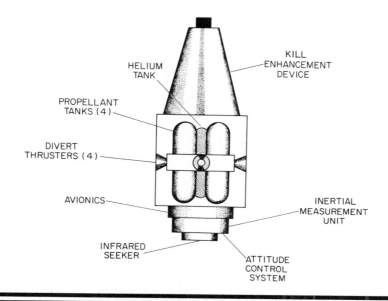

HELIUM
TANK

KILL
ENHANCEMENT
DEVICE

PROPELLANT
TANKS (4)

DIVERT
THRUSTERS (4)

AVIONICS

INERTIAL
MEASUREMENT
UNIT

INFRARED
SEEKER

ATTITUDE
CONTROL
SYSTEM

Fig. 7.1. Diagram of the payload of the Exoatmospheric Reentry Vehicle Interception System (ERIS) planned for the midcourse defense in a Phase I strategic defense deployment. A two-stage booster is used to boost it from the ground.

against a space background. SSTS will not be able to track the warheads lying in a direction toward the Earth because the Earth's emission of infrared radiation will mask it. The SSTS satellites may also carry some of the battle-management computers, allowing the complete tracking and target assignment for the weapons to be carried out on the SSTS.

3. High Endoatmospheric Defense Interceptor (HEDI). The terminal defense would consist of ground-launched kinetic-energy interceptors along with the Airborne Optical Adjunct for tracking the warheads (introduced in Chapter 4). A diagram of the planned HEDI interceptors is shown in Figure 7.2. Tremendous cooling will be required for using a homing-type vehicle in the atmosphere, since the heat of the rocket's flight through the atmosphere generates a strong local source of infrared radiation that may mask the homing device.

Early-deployment plans raised important questions about the cost of the deployment as well as the problems and weaknesses with Phase I deployment. These will be addressed in the next two sections.

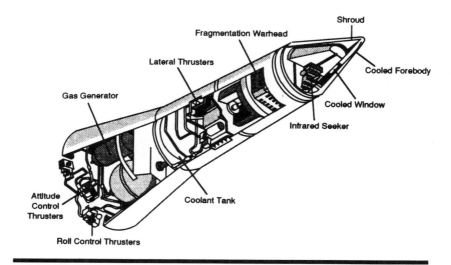

Fig. 7.2. Diagram of the payload of the High Endoatmospheric Defense Interceptor (HEDI) planned for a terminal
defense in a Phase I strategic defense deployment. A two-
stage booster is used to boost it from the ground. (Source:
*1989 Report to Congress on the Strategic Defense Initia-
tive*)

Cost Estimates for a Phase I Deployment

At least four cost estimates have been projected for
deployment of the Phase I defense, originally planned for the early or
mid-1990s. The first estimate was made just for the cost of the SBIs,
which will probably be the most expensive phase. The latter estimates have
been made on all three layers of the defense.

The estimate made by the SDIO was for the cost of the boost-phase
defense. The estimate assumed that 3,000 SBIs would be adequate, which
would be placed on 300 low-Earth-orbiting satellites (geosynchronous satellites are not possible for SBIs). Only a fraction would be accessible to
boost-phase missiles at any given time. Assuming that about one-third are
accessible, then the interceptors could take out 1,000 missiles, provided
that they are 100% accurate in destroying their target and that none of the
satellites are destroyed prior to a missile launch. This would be a 72% kill
under these ideal conditions. In reality, the accuracy will not approach

100%. Furthermore, ASATs and other countermeasures will be deployed if the United States deploys a Phase I defense.

The SDIO estimated the cost of a minimal Phase I defense initially at $110 billion, then in the fall of 1988 presented a stripped-down version to the Pentagon at an estimated cost of $69 billion. In the stripped-down version the number of space-based interceptors was reduced to 1,500, while the number of less expensive warhead interceptors was increased. The projected cost has been criticized as a gross underestimate because it assumes very low production costs and does not include many peripheral costs.

A separate estimate for the Phase I defense was put forward by the George Marshall Institute. They assumed 11,000 SBIs would be needed but proposed placing these on 220 satellites, increasing the concentration of interceptors on the satellites by a factor of 5. In addition, 13,000 ground-based interceptors would be used for the midcourse and terminal defense. The estimated cost for the system was put at $121 billion.[5] Important costs of developing and deploying these systems were not included in these estimates. The costs projections were labeled by several within the DOD and SDIO as unrealistic for the deployment of these systems.[6]

An estimate made by Lawrence Livermore Laboratory for a Phase I defense system included the costs of all three layers of the defense. For these three layers they estimate the cost to be $239 billion. This included 11,000 SBIs at $121 billion, 10,000 ERIS at $31 billion for the midcourse, and 3,000 HEDI at $87 billion for the terminal defense. HEDI is the most advanced system and will require the most research and testing to develop.[7]

Finally, an estimate was made by Johns Hopkins School for Advanced International Studies, as one of four possible defense systems that was studied. The estimate was made shortly before Phase I was officially adopted by the SDIO. The study group concluded that 95,600 interceptors based on 1,915 satellites were needed to have an effective boost-phase kill (>90%) when potential errors were considered. To reasonably ensure survival in an attack on the defense, an additional 9,575 decoy satellites would be required. Their estimate for this part of the defense was $598 million if it was designed to defend against ICBMs, SLBMs, and intermediate-range missiles. In addition, the ground-based defenses for the midcourse and terminal defense would cost an additional $169 billion, giving a total cost of $767 billion.[8]

The first three of these cost estimates contain only the direct costs of the defensive system, and not the required expenses for developing, deploying, and operating the system. They do not include the research and development costs needed for critical systems on the satellites, such as missile tracking, command and control, development of the interceptor and satellites, and operation and maintenance of the systems. They also exclude the costs of deploying systems of the defense.

The estimated 10 million pounds of material in a Phase I defense would require about 200 shuttle launches to complete. The Advanced Launch System (ALS) under development would reduce this by a factor of 4, but over 50 launches would still be required. The cost of the ALS itself is estimated at nearly $20 billion. Currently deployment of large masses into orbit costs about $3,000 per pound. The SDIO goal is to reduce that cost to $300 per pound with the ALS, although there is widespread skepticism that this goal can be achieved. The ALS will not be available until 1998 at the earliest and could not complete deployment of the Phase I defense until about 2005.[9]

The cost of maintaining the system in space, replacing defective parts, and ensuring constant reliability, will be expensive but has not been determined. Only the Johns Hopkins study includes estimates for these costs in deploying the system as well as the costs of providing minimum protection for the system. The cost of the Phase I system from the more realistic Johns Hopkins study estimate approaches $1 trillion. Yet this is only a Phase I defense, which would be followed by more comprehensive and advanced-phase deployments of undetermined costs.

The Marshall Institute report concluded that three layers of defense in this first phase could make the defense 90% effective in countering a missile attack by the Soviets. This assumes that no effective attack on the defense is made first. Even if it could be 90% effective, it would still allow over 1,500 warheads to hit the United States in an all-out attack, or more if the Soviets expand their missile force. This would do little to reduce the disastrous consequences of a nuclear war. It certainly would not be the population defense that former Secretary of Defense Weinberger insisted the Phase I defense was designed for.

Major Weaknesses and Problems with Phase I Deployment

Although the current technology of kinetic-energy weapons makes them more readily available in a defensive system, early deployment of a reliable defense with the three layers proposed is seriously flawed. The defense will require the systems outlined in Chapter 5 and will have the inherent weaknesses and vulnerabilities discussed. They will be subject to the countermeasures described in Chapter 6. Furthermore, the SDIO significantly lowered the performance requirements of many of the key elements for the defense in Phase I with the shift to a phased deployment.

The problems in software for battle management in a Phase I defense were analyzed in a 1988 study on phased deployment by the Office of Technology Assessment (OTA) (a follow-up to the 1985 study discussed in Chapter 1). Some of the stated conclusions of this study are as follows: "Ballistic missile defense battle management would be an extremely complex process. The number of objects, volume of space, and speed at which decisions would have to be made during a battle preclude most human participation. . . . Decisions about which weapons to use, when to use them, and against which targets would all have to be automated . . . the novelty of the technology it must control would impose a significant probability of software-induced catastrophe in the system's first real battle."

One of the principal findings stated in the summary: "The nature of software and experience with large complex software systems indicate that there would always be irresolvable questions about how dependable BMD software would be and about the confidence we could place in dependability estimates. Existing software systems, such as the long-distance telephone system, have become highly dependable only after extensive operational use and modification. In OTA's judgment, there would be a significant probability . . . that the first (and presumably only) time the BMD system were used in a real war, it would suffer a catastrophic failure."[10] There could be no confidence in the defense system.

An immediate problem created by early deployment is that it commits this country to a defensive system before key technological developments are available to allow an informed decision on the usefulness and wisdom of deploying a defense. This is in opposition to the goal set out for the research and technology phase of SDI, which was to provide answers to many unsolved technical problems and allow an informed decision on deployment. Early deployment locks in the U.S. commitment for a missile defense and preempts options for arms control negotiations in the future.

Paul Nitze, the senior arms control advisor in the Reagan administration, put forth a set of useful criteria for a defense at the World Affairs Council in February 1985. These are conditions that a defense must satisfy before it would by reasonable to deploy it. These criteria are:[11]

1. *Cost effectiveness.* The cost of the defense must be as cheap as the offensive forces it is designed to counter, so the offense has no incentive to add additional offensive capability to overwhelm it. If this is not satisfied, the offensive side would be encouraged to proliferate their capabilities, as well as add countermeasures to the defense.

2. *Survivability against attack.* The defense must be able to defend itself against major attacks and still be able to counter missiles after the attacks. If it cannot, the defense stations would be tempting targets for the Soviets, which would decrease stability.

3. *Stability in arms control.* The presence of a defense against ballistic missiles must not increase uncertainties in a crisis situation between the two sides, because these uncertainties may cause a serious error in judgment that leads to an accidental nuclear attack. In addition, a defense that increases the advantage to strike first further erodes this stability, encouraging an offensive buildup.

Congress enacted the Nitze criteria into a law forbidding deployment unless both the president and Congress certify that the system is survivable in the face of determined attack and cost-effective at the margin with respect to offensive buildup and countermeasures. The law was part of the Defense Authorization Act of 1986 (see Appendix 14 for the full statement of this law).[12]

Although it is highly questionable whether any defense satisfying these criteria can be developed in the foreseeable future, there is no question that the systems planned for early deployment will not satisfy these criteria. The cost estimates range from $239 billion to $767 billion for a Phase I defense, which will have to be followed up by expensive later phases. In contrast, the cost of the Soviets deploying 600 SS-24s and 600 SS-25s, almost doubling their ground-based offensive force, would be about $30 billion. It would cost several hundred billion dollars of extra defense to counter the offensive buildup. Even if the Phase I defense was effective against the current Soviet force, it could be beaten by a much less expensive Soviet buildup.

The only cost estimate that allows for a self-protection against attack is the Johns Hopkins study, which allows for five decoy satellites for every armed defense satellite. This might effectively counter an attack on the defense if the offense could not distinguish between the two types of satellites. However, the deployment of decoy satellites is not part of the planned Phase I deployment by the SDIO. Because of the vulnerability of critical systems required for tracking, command, and control, the SBIs could easily be crippled by such an attack, which would neutralize the defense.

Deploying a Phase I defense would be destabilizing to arms control. The cost of the system compared to the offensive buildup needed to overwhelm it would encourage that buildup. The Soviets could design the hypothetical force of 600 SS-24s and 600 SS-25s so that they would use fast-burn boosters at a cost of about $60 billion, compared to the cost of

$30 billion using conventional boosters. Advanced fast-burn boosters could be capable of burning out inside the atmosphere (for a 60-second boost-phase time), making them invulnerable to the SBIs' attack. This cost would still be 20% or less of the cost of the defense. In addition, the Soviets could upgrade their antisatellite weapons and introduce space mines at a much lower cost than the defense. The defense deployment will encourage these arms buildup actions. This will abrogate the prospects for deep bilateral cuts in nuclear arms that the United States and Soviet Union have been discussing in recent years.[13]

A determination of the number of SBIs needed to counter 250 new missiles of varying boost-phase times was made by David Spergel and George Field (see Appendix 15). The costs for the extra SBIs were estimated from the very conservative estimate made by the Hoover Institution of $6 million per interceptor. With the 180-second boost-phase time of SS-25s without fast-burn boosters, 7,000 new SBIs will be needed, at a cost of $42 billion, compared to a cost of $12.5 billion for the new missiles. If fast-burn boosters are used in the 250 missiles, then for a 90-second boost-phase time, 30,000 new SBIs will be needed, which will cost $180 billion. That can be compared to the $22.5 billion maximum for the new missiles with fast-burn boosters. If the fast-burn boosters allow the missiles to achieve a 60-second boost-phase time, the SBIs will be completely avoided.

The lowered standards and technological inadequacies for missile sensors and decoy discrimination systems seriously degrade the defense capability of effectively destroying the missiles, especially with appropriate countermeasures. It will be easier to camouflage the missiles with decoys, metal chaff, and smoke screens in the critical boost phase of the missiles when offense is most vulnerable. These countermeasures will be much less expensive than defensive upgrades to avoid them, encouraging the Soviets to take these measures.

In summary, many of the demanding problems that will have to be solved to make a missile defense feasible will clearly not be solved for a Phase I defense. Yet it will be expensive and will commit us to more expensive follow-up phases that will attempt to rectify many of the weaknesses of the Phase I defense.

Responses to Early-Deployment Planning

There were a number of responses to the planned early deployment of a missile defense by groups analyzing a missile defense, mostly negative. For example, just after the American Physical

Society study group had publicly released an in-depth analysis of the science and technology of directed-energy weapons, a more general statement was released by the general council to the American Physical Society. The resolution states the following: "Even a very small percentage of nuclear weapons penetrating a defense system would cause human suffering and death far beyond that ever seen on this planet. It is likely to be decades, if ever, before an effective, reliable, and survivable defensive system could be deployed. Development of prototypes or deployment of SDI components in a state of technological uncertainty risks enormous waste of financial and human resources."[14]

Ashton Carter, the Harvard physicist who prepared the Office of Technology Assessment report on ballistic missile defense in 1984, stated: "I see problems being swept under the rug in the interest of getting consensus on early deployment. It may be possible to put a system like this in place, but it is not clear that it would have any military value." Gerald Yonas, former chief scientist in the SDIO, similarly criticized early deployment as counterproductive to long-term stable development. Referring to early deployment as instant gratification, he stated that instead of early deployment, we should be examining and debating issues on capability, survivability, and feasibility.[15]

Frustration has come from scientists involved in long-term research to develop high-energy lasers and particle beams that were the focus of the first few years of SDI. Initiating the research programs required long-term planning and hiring, with the anticipation of long-term sustenance. With the early-deployment shift, the money in SDI was shifted more toward kinetic-energy-weapon development, and research on high-energy laser and particle beams was cut. For example, William Bartletta, one of the directors of beam-weapons research at Lawrence Livermore Laboratory criticized these "institutional gyrations" and cuts, stating that the antimissile program has a new twist in priorities every few years. One of the early plans was to have a $400-million free-electron laser facility at Lawrence Livermore by 1989, as well as a major test facility in New Mexico. The program was dropped at the onset of plans for early deployment.[16]

Accidental-Launch Protection System

A proposal was made in January 1988 before the Senate Armed Services Committee by Georgia Senator Sam Nunn, chairman of the committee, to explore a limited defense to protect against accidental or unauthorized nuclear launches. In making the proposal, he pointed out that slogans and theology had been substituted for technically sound scientific research. His proposal was made to be consistent with the 1972 ABM Treaty with possible minor modifications.[17]

The Accidental-Launch Protection System (ALPS) would consist of 100 ERIS (terminal-phase) launchers at Grand Forks, North Dakota, specified in the protocol to the ABM Treaty (Appendix 16). Such a system would likely be inadequate to counter accidental launches with targets on the East Coast or West Coast of the United States. The cost of this system was estimated at $16 billion for a minimum defense, or $37 billion for a high-quality system designed to protect the coasts as well.[18]

Many in Congress saw this proposal as much more rational than the proposed Phase I defense. It certainly would cost much less than a Phase I defense and would not present the strong encouragement for an offensive buildup that a strategic defense would. However, it is not clear whether this might form the "first phase of the first phase" — a first step in the deployment of a more complete first-phase defense.

The ALPS proposal for a significantly scaled-down defense is more attractive than other systems that are planned or envisioned under the Strategic Defense Initiative. It would not be destabilizing, would cost much less, and may fit in with arms control agreements with minor modifications. However, it will still be a major commitment in the federal budget. Before any decision is made on ALPS, full exploration should be made on other proposals for the prevention of accidental launches.

One such proposal for preventing accidental launches was put forth several years ago. In that proposal, all ballistic missiles would be fitted with a destruct mechanism that requires a unique secret code to activate. In the event of an accidental launch, the side making the accidental launch could destroy the missiles launched, or even communicate the codes for the launched missiles to the other side to destroy them if they are out of range. This could be enacted by an arms agreement. Installing such a protection mechanism in strategic missiles would be less costly and more reliable than an ALPS defense.

Brilliant Pebbles

In 1988 Lowell Wood of Lawrence Livermore Laboratory, working with Edward Teller, made a proposal for a new concept for a ballistic-missile boost-phase defense: to saturate space with a set of as many as 100,000 independent miniature battle stations, each packed with the technology to defend a zone of space independently. These devices would be built with advances in miniaturization of the technology, and are called Brilliant Pebbles. One purpose behind the Brilliant Pebbles proposal was to provide a system that eliminated the communication needed for target acquisition and tracking. This increases the survivability of the defense by avoiding jamming, interference, and other attacks on the communication links. Communication would still be necessary for intelligence and battle management.[19]

By configuring smaller miniaturized platforms with imaging systems, a supercomputer, energetic batteries, and a propulsion system, it was anticipated that low-cost, jam-resistant, nuclear-survivability, and high-maneuverability systems could be achieved. Making the devices smaller and lighter would decrease the ease of targeting in an attack on the defense and make it easier to deploy.

The decreased size is, however, accompanied by a sizable increase in numbers. Each Brilliant Pebble would weigh about 100 pounds (up from the original estimate of 5 pounds), so the total payload to be deployed will be 5–10 million pounds if 50,000–100,000 are deployed. The task of transporting such a system into orbit will be almost as large as that for the planned first-phase defense.

Current estimates are that each Brilliant Pebble would cost at least $500,000 to build. The number of Brilliant Pebbles deployed would need to be in the tens of thousands. For 100,000 Brilliant Pebbles, the direct cost of the defense is $50 billion, although the defense might get by with a smaller number. This boost-phase defense is estimated to be capable of taking out 30% of the missiles.

Although this advanced technological concept is more attractive than the boost-phase system proposed for Phase I deployment, it does not resolve many of the issues in deploying a defense. Deploying even a Brilliant Pebbles defense would be an expensive undertaking, and a 30% efficiency would mean that an effective midcourse and terminal defense would need to accompany it. If its only purpose is to protect against an accidental launch, it is less attractive than the ALPS proposal because it is a violation of the ABM Treaty (see Chapter 10). If its purpose is to provide a limited protection of our missile silos against a first strike, a 30% effectiveness may protect some of the missile silos and military installations against a first strike, although it is not clear that it is necessary for such protection or will significantly increase our capacity to retaliate in the event one occurs.

The idea of Brilliant Pebbles is classified by the SDIO as an advanced technology concept. Before it is possible, major scientific breakthroughs will be necessary in many areas, such as miniaturization, battle-management software, tracking, and homing. Although it may get around some countermeasures, there are several others available that will still be effective in avoiding it. Because it is an area defense, the offense could concentrate its launch in a small area to overwhelm it. The boost-phase launch could be accompanied by many boost-phase decoys, along with mechanisms such as aluminum chaff and smoke clouds to hide the missiles and to lead the defense astray. The attack could also be staged, with the first wave being used to make a hole in the defense and the second stage to break through. The concept is novel but does not get around many of the difficulties faced in deploying a defense.

Several recent reviews have raised questions about the technical feasibility of Brilliant Pebbles, including the Air Force Space Division and its contractors for the SBI, Martin Marietta and Rockwell. Questions and doubts have been raised from tests about the capability of the Brilliant Pebbles sensors to meet acquisition and tracking requirements. Other doubts have been raised about communication between the Brilliant Pebbles and the autonomous command and control capabilities each Brilliant Pebble must have.[20]

In a 1989 editorial, Congressman Charles Bennett of Florida addressed the new idea as a red herring to attempt to divert the cuts the SDI budget was undergoing to the funding of a new program. This was what SDI was billed at in 1983, and after spending $17 billion under SDI, the new concept may be a way of turning around the program's first real cuts after years of rapid growth.[21]

CHAPTER 8

Offensive Uses of Defensive Weapons

In previous chapters the proposed space-based systems for a missile defense, along with their requirements for this task and potential weaknesses, were examined. It was shown that many requirements of these systems lead to prohibitive costs, while certain requirements are so demanding that they may not be achievable with anything resembling current or anticipated technology. The Soviets will have ample opportunity to foil and counter the defensive systems, normally at a small cost compared to the cost of the defense itself.

However, ignoring the major difficulties discussed in previous chapters, suppose that all necessary breakthroughs are made to solve the major problems, allowing the achievement of an effective defense that allows protection of essential military components. Will the United States have reached the goal of enhanced deterrence, which many associated with SDI have set, through the development and building of these weapons? Will we be able to make the defensive transition in which the only arms buildup is in defensive weapons to counter offensive weapons?

A strategic defense will in fact produce a continuation, probably even an acceleration, of the offensive nuclear arms buildup, for two reasons. One is that the cost of defense is so much more expensive than the cost of offense that the uncertainty created by the deployment of a defense will cause the other side to counter with an offensive buildup. They know that they can do so for much less cost than the side with the defense can to counter the extra offense.

The second reason is that the defensive technologies will be much more useful in certain offensive capacities with counterforce weapons or antisatellite weapons before they can be useful in a defensive capacity.

These uses are clearly destabilizing to the international nuclear arms balance and will provide the other side with a motivation for a massive arms buildup.

Offensive Buildup Response and the Nuclear Triad

Chapter 6 discussed how Soviet perceptions of the way a missile defense might give the United States a nuclear superiority would encourage an offensive buildup by the Soviet Union, and the much lower cost of the offensive forces than the defense needed to counter them will provide a significant motivation for that buildup. The nature of this offensive response will be influenced by the triad of offensive nuclear forces.

The basing of nuclear weapons on land, sea, and air forms the *nuclear triad,* an important part of military strategy. The United States places an approximately equal emphasis on all three legs of this triad. The basis for this strategy is that any weakness inherent in one type of basing is compensated for by strengths in the other types of basing. Thus, for example, the Soviets cannot have any confidence that a preemptive first strike on our land-based forces (which is only about a quarter of our nuclear forces) has any hope of being effective, because the sea and air defenses can completely destroy the Soviet Union in a retaliatory strike just as assuredly as the Soviet Union can destroy the United States with the land-based strike.

The Soviet Union does not put the same emphasis on all three legs of the triads: 64% of their nuclear weapons are in land-based forces, and only 36% in the other two legs of the triad; 28% are sea-based, and 8% are air-based. Part of this emphasis is due to geographic considerations: The Soviet Union does not have as convenient an access to the seas as the United States does, and their North Sea access is impeded during the colder part of the year. Thus their sea-based nuclear-force development is somewhat inhibited and its usefulness is limited. On the other hand, they have more land on which to test and deploy missiles than the United States does.

Even if a strategic defense could effectively counter the land-based missiles, the defense against sea-based missiles will be much more difficult. The reason for these difficulties is that for sea-based missiles the location from which the missiles will be fired is not fixed and the nuclear submarines will be closer to the United States, so that flight paths and time of flight is much shorter. Instead of a half hour to attempt to take out almost all of the land-based offense, that time will be reduced to as short as 10 minutes.

Using a boost-phase and midcourse defense against sea-launched ballistic missiles requires defenses at appropriate locations that depend on
where the submarines are when the missiles are fired. Probably only a
terminal defense can be used against these missiles, so the defense will be
only a single shot. The laddering scheme discussed in Chapter 4 would be
effective in getting many of the offensive weapons through.

Defense against bombers and cruise missiles is almost beyond the
realm of a strategic defense because of the difficulty of targeting low-
flying crafts, given their undetermined paths and maneuverability in an
unpredictable manner. Site defenses would have to be used, and paths can
be devised to avoid these defenses. Hence the defense can at best counter
only a low percentage of these targets. In addition, there are many ways to
get nuclear weapons into a country, such as trucks and suitcases. Because
of these limitations, the best that can be developed is a partial defense of
questionable effectiveness. The Reagan goal of population protection is
totally unfeasible, and the use of this defense to protect essential military
installations and enhance deterrence will likely be unreliable.

The fact that a strategic defense has much more difficulty countering
the 28% of Soviet nuclear weapons in the sea-based leg of their triad and
can counter little of the 8% air-based leg means that discussions of "95%
effectiveness" of the defense can be deceptive. What such numbers usually
mean is 95% of the 64% land-based force and a much lower percentage of
the 28% sea-based force. If we assume a 50% effectiveness in the countering of the sea-based forces and 10% of the air-based forces, then there
is a 75% effectiveness against the total Soviet force. Since the Soviets have
enough weapons to destroy us 60 times over (as we do them), such a
reduction would correspond to their being able to destroy the United
States only 16 times over. The difference is meaningless in realistic terms.

An illustration of what these numbers mean in a full-scale nuclear
war can be made. Suppose that the Soviets fired 10,000 strategic warheads
at the United States (they also have many more tactical warheads) and that
we have built a very successful defense that has a very high 95% accuracy
against the ICBMs that the Soviets would launch. (Soviet countermeasure
and difficulties discussed in previous chapters would make this assumed
accuracy unrealistic.) A lower accuracy would be available for the more-
difficult-to-counter sea-based weapons, but suppose a very good 90% effectiveness could be achieved against them (also unrealistically high). The
strategic defense will not be effective against air-based weapons of
bombers and cruise missiles, but suppose the United States completely
lines the shores with antiaircraft capabilities, including high-powered lasers that operate in the atmosphere and kinetic-energy devices built from
SDI technology that could take out a large percentage of the airplanes.

Assume a very optimistic 75% of the air attack could be taken out. The net effect would be that 800 strategic warheads would get through, enough to completely destroy the United States! It is also well above the threshold estimated for the onset of "nuclear winter" (discussed in Chapter 12).

In addition to the large number of strategic warheads getting through there are the tactical warheads that could follow this up, which would number several thousand even if the same percentages of them could be destroyed. There are so many more strategic warheads alone than are needed for complete destruction of the country that the strategic defense would not provide any protection in a major nuclear war, even if such a highly accurate defense could be built.

However, in the political reasoning that both the United States and the Soviet Union have applied in the arms race, perceived differences in nuclear strengths are considered important. Each side reasons that if the other side has greater strength in terms of some arbitrary way of assigning numerical values to the nuclear arsenals held by each power, then a major defense spending and development program is necessary to narrow the perceived gap. This way of reasoning, along with the conflicting national and political interests of the United States and the Soviet Union, has fueled the arms race since its inception.

It is the political concern over a possible nuclear superiority of the United States that is one of the reasons the Soviets object to the development of a strategic defense by the United States. If such a defense could theoretically take out 50%–75% of the Soviet force, it would reduce their effective nuclear strength 50%–75%, giving clear nuclear superiority to the United States. Given the possibility of this state of affairs (and Soviet perceptions of this capability may have little to do with reality), the Soviets will embark on a massive offensive buildup to catch up with the United States. For this reason, along with the economic trade-off of offense versus defense, an effective strategic defense will lead to a major arms buildup by the Soviets.

When the Soviets engage in this massive arms buildup, where will they put the emphasis? In bombers and cruise missiles, which cannot be effectively countered by the strategic defense. Efforts will also be made to build less expensive single-warhead missiles (to overwhelm the critical boost-phase defense) and base them in ways to maximize their ability of surviving the boost-phase defense. After the Soviets have made a major buildup in these areas, we will be back into the same condition we are in now without the strategic defense, even if an initially effective defense system is deployed. After the offensive buildup, the defense would then be ineffective against a sizable portion of the Soviet nuclear force.

The amount of the economic resources that would be taken up by a new arms race expansion resulting from a strategic defense would be staggering. As discussed in Chapter 6, the side that focuses most on developing a defensive system in such a race would lose.

The Counterforce Strategy

The anticipated offensive buildup in response to defensive weapons has an interesting parallel on a smaller scale in recent history. Strategic missiles have become increasingly accurate with technological development over the last decade or more. This has led to a nuclear strategy shift from earlier days, when each side targeted the other side's cities (the *countervalue* strategy), to the more recent strategy that emphasizes the targeting of the other side's military forces and installations (the *counterforce* strategy).

The increasing accuracy of the missiles and resulting strategy shift created a concern in the United States over the vulnerability of our stationary land-based missiles caused by counterforce targeting. It was felt in the 1970s in the Defense Department that at some point in the future the Soviets would be able to make a preemptive first strike against these missiles (to destroy them before they are usable). One of the reasons for the development of the concern for a preemptive first strike has to do with the advantage of surprise. The country making the first strike will always have the advantage because it can choose the time of the attack for its own advantage and because the attacked side must respond quickly to ensure it gets off a full retaliation. Some instability has been created in the nuclear arms race as each side worries that the other might take out its missiles in its silos through a preemptive first strike.

It was the concern over our land-based missile system in the mid-1970s that led to the proposal for the Mobile-X (MX) missile. The idea was to have a new missile system based in a site with 10 times as many silos as missiles and an interconnecting track system (the racetrack configuration) allowing for the shuffling of missiles between the silos. This would mean that the Soviets, who would not know which silos contained the missiles, would have to target all of the silos in order to have a reasonable hope of destroying the missiles. Presumably, then, the survival of our land-based missiles would be assured, since the Soviets do not have enough missiles to target all of our MX silos and Minuteman silos at the same time.

These concerns about a preemptive first strike are ill-founded, however, when one considers the fact the United States has superiority over the Soviet Union in sea- and air-based forces that are always available for retaliation. Furthermore, there is an extremely low probability of a completely successful preemptive first strike against just the land-based missiles.[1] An analysis based on 1982 figures for number of warheads showed that for a first strike by either the Soviet Union or the United States there is considerably more than adequate retaliation for total destruction of the other side.[2]

The most important factor is the perception of a threat, since such perceptions lead to political decisions made in the arms race, not necessarily factual realities. These perceptions of threat, real or imagined, are a major driving force for the arms race. The concerns and perceptions that would develop with the deployment of a missile defense would be a strong driving force, given the grave nature of the perceived threat.

The new class of counterforce weapons that are highly accurate and targeted against the other side's strategic missiles and military targets commonly go by the name *first-strike weapons*. This is a result of the fact that they have as great a potential use for a first strike than as a retaliatory second strike in response to a first strike. The MX missile falls into that category; it is about 25 times more accurate than the Minuteman III.

Prior to the Reagan administration the proposed use for the MX missiles involved placing them in a cluster of protective shelters, to be shuttled around in a racetrack configuration to conceal their silo locations. This plan was canceled during the Reagan administration and replaced with one in which the missiles are deployed in vulnerable Minuteman silos. In 1986, 50 MXs were deployed in these silos. In this mode the missiles are just as vulnerable as the Minuteman to a first strike by the other side. Yet it was the vulnerability of these silos that led to the development of MX missiles in the first place. Hence the only advantage that the MX missiles provide in this basing is their high accuracy, an advantage that is primarily useful in a first strike.

The MX missile is much more lethal than the Minuteman III in its ability to target and destroy Soviet silos. This will increase the chances that the Soviets would want to take them out with a preemptive first strike in case of a major crisis between the two sides if they were deployed in large numbers. Thus they are potentially a destabilizing force in the nuclear arms balance. As McGeorge Bundy (special assistant to the president on national security in the Kennedy administration) once commented in connection with these missiles, "For almost thirty years we have made survivable second-strike strength our central strategic standard. Are we now to move, in a cloud of consensus prose and good intentions, to a non-survivable first-strike system?"[3] The MX may be much more useful in a first strike by the United States than in retaliating against a first strike by the Soviets.

Current plans are to place the MX missiles deployed in Minuteman silos onto a rail-garrison system being developed by Boeing Aerospace under a contract awarded to the company in 1987. Part of the MX missiles originally planned have been replaced by the newer Midgetman missile. In contrast to the MX (which carries 10 MIRVed warheads) the Midgetman is designed to carry only one warhead but can be modified to carry three warheads. The missile is undergoing flight testing and should be ready for deployment in the mid-1990s. Current plans are to deploy 500 Midgetman missiles on trucks, to be launched from the interstates.[4]

Several alternate modes were considered for the MX before the decision was made to base it in the rail-garrison mode. One alternative mode for ensuring survivability of the MX that was studied was protecting it with a ground-based ballistic-missile defense for the terminal phase of the missiles. This would be a point defense, selectively defending certain missiles heavily while leaving others undefended. (The Soviets would not know which missiles are defended and probably could not overcome the defended missiles since they would not know which ones to saturate their attack upon.) Of course, if this defense can work effectively, it hardly provides a justification for the development of the MX (on the basis of providing a survivable land-based retaliation) because the defense would work just as well for the Minuteman missiles. The United States would not need the MX to ensure survivability of its retaliation.

Strategic Defense and First-Strike Weapons

There is an important danger posed by the deployment of a missile defense along with first-strike weapons. That arises because of a critical connection between the two systems. As mentioned before, there is a very low probability either that a preemptive first strike by one side would succeed in gaining the upper hand in the nuclear exchange or that a strategic defense would be effective in stopping a first strike by the other side. On the other hand, a side with both the first-strike weapons and a strategic defense system could with much greater effectiveness make a preemptive first strike and use the defense to counter the crippled retaliation by the attacked side. This offensive capability of strategic defense weapons would be much more feasible than the defensive use, and in the event of a major crisis between the United States and the Soviet Union, there would be a temptation to use the strategic missile defense in this offensive manner if both systems were deployed.

Even if an effective missile defense can be developed and deployed, the system would reach the stage where it is effective in this preemptive first-strike offensive use before it would be effective for use in a defensive mode. Not only does a preemptive first strike make the strategic defense much more effective in taking out weapons launched by the other side, but in a preemptive first strike the offense would have the advantage of surprise, whereas in the use of a missile defense purely in a defensive mode, the attacker has the advantage of surprise. Thus, strategic "defense" weaponry has a much greater offensive potential than a defensive potential, so it is more offensive than defensive in character.

In terms of nuclear stability, it matters little whether it is realistically possible to use strategic defense and first-strike systems in this offensive manner. Careful consideration of scenarios for the use of strategic defense weaponry in an offensive manner in connection with a preemptive first strike reveals that this venture is very unlikely to succeed. Such a combined attack could destroy at most the land-based missile systems (fixed-based) of the other side and conceivably a significant portion of the sea-based missiles. But at a minimum, a substantial portion of air-based systems and sea-based systems would be available for retaliation in sufficient numbers to destroy the other side.

However, it is the perception that such a combined offensive attack could be effective that would be destabilizing to the arms race and international situation. The reality of this capacity may be unimportant. The Soviet military will use a worst-case scenario for analyzing our intentions with these forces, and the resulting increased tensions between the two sides make an accidental nuclear war more likely. The Soviet fears of this scenario, shortly after the Strategic Defense Initiative began, led former Premier Chernenko to claim in early 1985: "In its substance this is an offensive or, to be more precise, an aggressive concept. The aim is to try to disarm the other side and deprive it of a capability to retaliate in the event of nuclear aggression against it. To put it simply, the aim is to acquire a capability to deliver a nuclear strike counting on impunity with an anti-ballistic missile shield to protect oneself from retaliation. . . ."[5] Later statements by Premier Gorbachev and other Soviet officials have expressed beliefs that the defense systems are threatening and destabilizing, although they have been tempered by realizations of the difficulties in building an effective missile defense along with the fact that our first-strike missile forces are small.

One of the earlier concerns in the United States after the Strategic Defense Initiative was that a strategic defense system coupled with a first-strike capability might motivate the Soviets into going to a launch-on-warning policy. The reason was that the Soviets would fear that 90% or more of their strategic nuclear capability could be wiped out by a preemptive strike coupled with a defense against their diminished ballistic missile retaliation. The Soviets would know that their missiles would be of greater use before a large number of them are destroyed by the preemptive strike, so that if they countered before they were hit, they could have more confidence that large numbers of their land-based missiles would get through the defense and out of the range of the attacking missiles and electromagnetic pulses associated with the nuclear explosions. Hence, in any crisis situation they would launch the retaliation on warning of a nuclear attack.

Neither the United States nor the Soviet Union has had such a policy, and any decision to retaliate to a possible launch by the other side would not be made until after early-warning systems have confirmed that such an attack is under way. This policy by the two countries has played a crucial role in avoiding a nuclear war. However, instabilities in the nuclear balance that create significant uncertainties in the critical moments when a decision has to be made were a reason for concern about the Soviets going to a launch-on-warning policy in a delicate or crisis situation.[6] This situation would significantly increase the likelihood of accidental nuclear war.

There are contradictions between the espoused purposes of a missile defense and its potential consequences. Former President Reagan repeatedly made the claim that the purpose of a missile defense is to protect populations against a nuclear attack by the other side, to get around the existing condition of mutually assured destruction (MAD). This of course is a condition that we have accepted and lived with for the last two decades, despite the feeling of many that the acronym MAD is a suitable description of the situation. The president posed SDI as a way to get around MAD, although the claim of protecting populations is widely recognized as fantasy.

The Department of Defense (DOD) generally recognizes that populations cannot be protected and has set goals to the strategic defense program that contradict Reagan's purpose: ensuring survivability (hence reinforcing mutually assured destruction) by using a missile defense to protect against the possibility of a successful preemptive first strike by the other side. This is a more modest objective than the population defense, and it is open to question whether the missile defense is necessary or useful for this objective.

There is no danger of a preemptive first strike's taking out retaliation in the absence of a strategic defense, although fears of that possibility on both sides have a destabilizing effect on arms race trends. The two declared purposes of missile defense contradict each other: one is not achievable, and the other appears unnecessary and fails to justify the expense involved. Not only will a strategic defense contribute little to ensuring survivability by protecting against a preemptive first strike, but it has greater prospects for aiding a preemptive first strike than for helping to ensure survivability! Both sides have first-strike weapons, with MX and Trident II missiles in the U.S. strategic forces and SS-24 and SS-25 missiles in the Soviet strategic forces. With these missiles the nuclear instability will increase with the deployment of a strategic defense by either side. It should be avoided to reduce the possibility of nuclear war between the two sides.

Antisatellite Weapons and Nuclear Stability

The United States and the Soviet Union have been engaged in the development of antisatellite weapons (ASATs) for many years now. The approach that has been used is different for the two sides, and the United States has had considerably greater success in recent years.

The United States has been involved in the development of ASATs since the late 1950s. The first one was the satellite interceptor (SAINT) device. The object of this device was to shoot an interceptor up when the Soviets launched one of their satellites. Upon interception, the satellite would be destroyed if it contained a nuclear warhead for use against the United States, but would be left alone if it was for peaceful uses. A few years later, after over $100 million had been spent on it and the many technical problems remained unsolvable, it was abandoned. In 1963 some changes were made in the Nike-Ajax missile, which had been developed for use as an early ABM system, to make an ASAT out of it. Secretary McNamara asked for deployment of these ASATs. The next year, this had been updated into the Thor missile.

The ASATs development efforts had concentrated on using nuclear warheads to destroy the target satellites. However, in the earlier 1960s an understanding of the effects of electromagnetic pulse (EMP) produced by nuclear explosions developed, and it was realized that the satellites could not be destroyed without major damage to other nearby systems. An effort went into using conventional weapons on the Thor missile, but it was soon realized that accuracy was too poor for this to be of use. These approaches were abandoned in 1974.[7]

The Soviet Union ASAT program began in 1968 and involves the development of ASATs that are satellites equipped with explosive devices. In order to destroy the target satellite, the ASAT uses co-orbital interception, where the ASAT maneuvers from its orbit into the orbit of the target satellite. Such maneuvering would take more than an hour, and the U.S. satellites would likely have ample warning to take evasive measures. This orbit manipulation technique is a feasible way to attack low-Earth-orbit

U.S. satellites (a few hundred miles up), but for sufficiently high-orbit satellites (such as the geosynchronous early-warning satellites that hover over the Soviet Union) the incredible difficulty of such maneuvering makes it highly impractical if not impossible. Thus, only the low-altitude satellites are threatened by this ASAT. This ASAT will require additional development before it will be operational since the Soviets have had difficulties in the development of the guidance and control systems.[8]

The United States developed an effective antisatellite system that became operational in 1987. It consists of a miniature homing vehicle on a two-stage booster rocket that is carried aboard an F-15 aircraft. To kill a satellite, the rocket is launched toward the satellite (the expected position based upon the known trajectory), and when it is in the vicinity of the satellite, a computer equipped with artificial intelligence determines its target. The rocket homes in on that target with automatic course corrections and destroys it by a head-on collision. Most of the present Soviet satellites would be vulnerable to this ASAT.

The problem posed by the development of ASATs is that they put satellites in danger that play a vital role in current nuclear stability. Both sides depend upon their satellites for early warning of a nuclear attack, treaty verification, crisis monitoring, reconnaissance (spying), communication, and navigation. All of these provide vital information on the other side's activities and have been an essential link in the arms control process. Without such knowledge it is always natural to assume the worst about what the other side is doing. In the event of a crisis, there would be a strong temptation for one side to deny information to the other side by knocking out its satellites. Such an eventuality would greatly magnify the chances of a crisis leading to a nuclear war. It is thus important that the development of these weapons be stopped by bilateral agreements to reduce the risk of nuclear war.

A problem that must be addressed in any kind of arms control treaty is that of verification. The satellite capabilities of the both sides currently appear adequate for monitoring and verifying compliance with arms control treaties. However, with the U.S. ASATs, this is a difficult problem because they would be hidden from observation. Because of this problem, the negotiation of a treaty banning ASAT weapons has become more complicated, but such a ban is needed to provide the nuclear stability that is available through close satellite monitoring.

Strategic Defense and Antisatellite Weapons

The problem of ASATs is aggravated by the development of a strategic defense because the technology that is being developed for the defense is also quite useful for second- and third-generation ASATs. Furthermore, if a strategic defense could be developed, satellites are much more vulnerable to an attack by the defense. The reason is that the capability of destroying slower-moving satellites, following a totally known trajectory and with limited maneuvering ability available on sudden notice, would be developed long before the capability to destroy more rapidly moving missiles, which are launched without prior warning in great numbers and have greater maneuverability in their critical early stages. New, more threatening offensive capabilities will arise from strategic-defense development before useful defensive capabilities can be achieved.

It is much harder to defend satellites against ASATs than it is to defend missiles against strategic defense weapons. An aggressor using ASAT weapons to counter satellites can strike with little warning and has the advantage of surprise. Furthermore, satellites necessarily contain sensitive optics and communication systems for their functions, and these are very vulnerable in an attack. Taking out either the optical or communication capabilities of a satellite renders it useless.

Technologies that are undergoing research for strategic defense also have potential capabilities for future generation ASATs. Space-based and ground-based lasers could be developed for ASAT capability with less-demanding requirements and fewer constraints. Space-based lasers would need a significantly smaller number of orbiting stations, lower beam brightness, and a smaller fuel supply than that needed for a missile defense. Ground-based lasers would need a significantly lower beam brightness. X-ray lasers could also be used to "pop-up" and attach satellites.[9]

Homing rockets are already used on the American ASATs, and BMD developments of homing rockets will also provide greater ASAT capability. The newer concept of Brilliant Pebbles will also have significant ASAT capabilities if developed. These devices could defend an area against military satellites more easily than they could defend an area against a missile attack.

If the United States deploys a strategic defense, it is very likely that both sides will deploy upgraded antisatellite weapons. The Soviets will build and deploy upgraded versions to help in countering the space-based components of the strategic defense of the United States and the global surveillance that will be necessary to accompany it. The United States will deploy upgraded versions because the technological developments made for the defense will be very useful for advanced antisatellite weapons and as a natural response to the Soviet deployment.

If the United States continues the development of a strategic defense, it will decrease the stability provided by satellite monitoring, for two reasons. First, no ASAT treaty will be negotiable because of the close link between strategic defense and ASAT technologies. Second, ASAT technology that becomes available from strategic-defense development will be applied to ASATs deployed. The danger of nuclear war will become much greater because the satellites that provide stability and that would provide vital information in a major crisis would be threatened.

Just as in the case of first-strike weapons, the offensive ASAT capabilities produced by strategic-defense development will be available prior to the time the defensive capabilities are. The reason is that in the case of a strategic defense, it is the offense launching the missiles that has the advantage of surprise. Once the launch occurs, the missile trajectories must be determined quickly in order to have any hope of countering them. On the other hand, ASAT weapons have the capability to surprise-attack the satellites. The satellite must be able to detect the attack sufficiently quickly and determine some details of it in time to counter it, whereas the satellite trajectory will be known ahead of time and the time of the antisatellite launch made at will. The sudden attack on vulnerable satellites is much harder to counter than the responsive missile-defense attack on the sudden launch of the missiles.

The satellites (space platforms) used in a strategic defense are very vulnerable to an ASAT attack. The components of a space defensive system that engages the missiles will have to be in low Earth orbit to have access to the missiles and thus will be sitting ducks for a precursor attack before missiles are launched. If the Soviets develop X-ray-laser rockets, they can launch the rockets to attack the defense satellites before a missile launch. The X-ray-laser rockets can rise out of the atmosphere before they are all destroyed by the defense and make a direct attack on the defense, significantly hampering or destroying its capabilities before the missiles are launched. The development of technologies for a strategic defense by both sides will inevitably provide each side with capabilities for attacking a space-based defense as well as attacking satellites used for early warning, communication, reconnaissance, and treaty verification. The United States and Soviet Union have over 150 satellites used for these military purposes.[10]

In the extensive report released by the Office of Technology Assessment in 1988 after two years of research, it was concluded that deployment of ballistic-missile defenses in orbit (which will be required for a boost-phase defense) will spur an arms race in space military weapons.

The deployment would produce an intense competition where the Soviets develop and deploy the same technology to attack the U.S. defense satellites and sensors. A Phase I defense would soon become obsolete because of Soviet attack capabilities and countermeasures, whereas later-phase defenses have not been shown to be feasible. In addition, there are the inherent difficulties in developing the software, as discussed in Chapters 6 and 7.[11]

There are additional offensive uses for the military technology developed for a ballistic-missile defense. Laser technologies that penetrate the atmosphere can be developed to accurately strike ground targets, start widespread fires, and conduct attacks on national leaders. They could be used to destroy key airborne control centers, as well as fuel storage tanks, radars, communication systems, ships, and troop concentrations.[12]

Thus the development of a strategic defense will provide major nuclear instability before any defensive capability is available. In addition to the jeopardizing of treaty negotiations and the confidence that one could have in compliance with those treaties, the uncertainty created by the resulting vulnerabilities to critical satellites might lead to an accidental nuclear launch in a major crisis that develops between the United States and the Soviet Union. Given the global concern about the possibility of nuclear destruction, it is quite undesirable to have systems that would significantly increase this possibility.

CHAPTER 9

Third-Generation Nuclear Weapons

In the summer of 1986 Senator John Kerry pointed out that President Reagan had claimed on many public occasions that the Strategic Defense Initiative is non-nuclear. For example, in an address to Congress in late 1985, he stated that he had informed Gorbachev at the summit that "SDI has nothing to do with offensive weapons; instead, we are investigating non-nuclear defensive systems that only threaten offensive missiles, not people."[1]

The former president often claimed that the only purpose of SDI is to defend ourselves against nuclear missiles, and originally set the goal of making nuclear weapons "impotent and obsolete." However, a substantial part of SDI has been devoted to developing a dangerous new generation of nuclear weapons, and they will be much less useful for defense than for offense.

The atomic bomb was the first generation, the hydrogen bomb the second generation of nuclear weapons. Certain programs in SDI are devoted to developing third-generation nuclear weapons. These new nuclear weapons have strong potential for use in the offensive mode and will likely create a new direction for the arms race.

Nuclear Weapon Development in SDI

A significant fraction of SDI research and development is on schemes that utilize a nuclear explosion to power them. The example introduced in Chapter 3 is the X-ray laser. A fraction of the energy of the nuclear explosion powers the laser, and the effect of the laser is to concentrate the power into one narrow direction. This directing of explosive power creates a destructive intensity that is much greater than a nuclear explosion alone, in which the power spreads out in all directions. For example, in the X-ray laser it is theoretically possible to produce power intensity in the direction of the beam 100 million times as great as it would be from a normal nuclear explosion if the laser is only 1% efficient in its usage of the power of the nuclear explosion! Anything in the beam's path within a few hundred kilometers that is not adequately shielded will be destroyed by the very high power concentration in the X-ray beam.

Third-generation nuclear weapons are ones that enhance certain aspects of a nuclear explosion to provide greater power for specific military purposes. Examples are the neutron bomb, in which the neutron radiation is significantly enhanced; the EMP weapon, in which the electromagnetic pulse of the explosion is enhanced; and the new class of directed-energy nuclear weapons such as the X-ray laser, in which part of the power of the nuclear detonation is enhanced by directing it.[2]

In addition to the X-ray laser, directed-energy nuclear weapons are also under development for producing powerful particle beams and high-speed kill vehicles. For particle-beam weapons of the form discussed in Chapter 3, it would be a difficult task to launch a satellite with a powerful particle accelerator needed to create a particle beam of intense power fluence (see Glossary) for use in a defense. However, when the beam is powered by a nuclear explosion, this task becomes much easier.

The X-ray-laser and particle-beam directed-energy weapons are envisioned as part of a defense, but previous chapters discussed their limits for use in this capacity. The X-ray laser cannot access the missile in its vulnerable boost phase because of the tremendous fuel reserves required for short boost-phase missiles. It can be used against reentry vehicles in the midcourse. However, as discussed in Chapter 4, the intense X-rays get absorbed totally in a very thin layer of the target's surface, causing the layer to explode. Shielding can potentially be accomplished with a thin false outer surface and a protecting layer, so that the outer shield explodes and the inner warhead is protected from that explosion. Multiple thin shields separated by protective layers could be used to counter multiple attacks.

These shields against the X-ray laser certainly do not guarantee survivability. However, they do significantly reduce the warhead destruction by the X-ray beam and help ensure that at least some of the warheads will survive. That is all that is necessary for a nuclear attack to be effective.

A countermeasure to a particle-beam boost-phase defense was mentioned in Chapter 3. The defense could be effectively countered by a high-altitude nuclear explosion in the atmosphere, which would have enough atmosphere out to the location of the particle-beam defenses to completely scatter the very intense particle beam in all directions. Therefore, the X-ray laser and probably the particle beam would not be effective for use on the boost-phase defense and only have uses in the midcourse defense.

However, the limits on the usefulness of these weapons in a strategic defense do not preclude them from being potent offensive weapons. The X-ray-laser and nuclear particle-beam systems are very powerful against anything that is not properly protected or cannot be protected. They would make deadly ASAT weapons. Satellite communication systems with their antennae and sensitive electronics cannot be protected, nor can their optical or infrared sensors. Taking out these functions renders a satellite useless. Yet satellites are crucial for early warning of a nuclear attack, spying, verifying treaties, and worldwide military communication. The intense destructive power of third-generation nuclear weapons could easily devastate critical systems on satellites.

In another nuclear program in SDI, code-named Prometheus, a nuclear explosion powers a large number of pellets to very high speed in one direction, which pulverize almost anything in their path. This is referred to as the *nuclear shotgun,* although the pellets can easily travel 1,000 times faster than the pellets in a shotgun, exploding on any impact. The explosion may be carried out underground, with the very fast pellets launched through a barrel rising to the surface. This "shotgun" pellet weapon is capable of destroying reentry vehicles, but it would be most effective in destroying aircraft and satellites.[3]

In an offensive mode, these weapons always have the advantage of surprise, do not have to take out the large number of protected objects necessary for defense, and do not need the very high accuracy that is required for a defense. They represent the next deadly step in the buildup of offensive nuclear weapons. The X-ray laser and Prometheus have undergone underground nuclear testing at the Nevada Test Site (NTS) and provide a major opposition to a comprehensive test ban, which can help stop the buildup of bigger and better nuclear weapons.

Consequences of the New Nuclear Weapons

The nuclear-explosion X-ray laser has been called a weapon "for the twenty-first century" because its potential uses in a nuclear force could make it an important part of a future nuclear arsenal. Research under SDI on the X-ray laser, Prometheus, and nuclear-powered particle-beam weapons are the beginning of a class of directed-energy nuclear weapons that could be developed and built in the future.

X-ray and particle-beam weapons powered by a nuclear explosion cannot penetrate the atmosphere, so objects on the surface of the Earth are safe from these weapons. However, a third-generation nuclear weapon under development enhances the electromagnetic pulse (EMP) in a high-altitude explosion, which can travel along the Earth's magnetic-field line to distant targets. The intense EMP is primarily in the microwave frequency range, so it can penetrate the atmosphere and be used to destroy objects on the ground. This weapon could be used to paralyze military installations and cities over hundreds of miles by knocking out all electrical and electronic systems in the area. It could be used to destroy critical electronics of missiles in their silos, possibly taking out the retaliatory capacity of the other side more effectively than first-strike weapons that both sides are concerned about.[4]

In addition, the EMP-enhanced nuclear weapon could be used to knock out critical systems on a defense against strategic missiles as well as on any important satellite used for a military function. Chapter 4 discussed the use of high-altitude nuclear explosions to counter the defense in the terminal phase. An EMP-enhanced nuclear weapon would be even more effective in paralyzing the terminal defense, extending the long-term blackouts for high-altitude explosions to a greater area. A high-altitude nuclear explosion with an EMP-enhanced weapon could also be used to counter tracking and communication in the midcourse phase by blacking out the signals.

Other potential varieties and uses of third-generation nuclear weapons may be developed. These include weapons using enhanced gamma-ray emissions from high-altitude bursts directed against targets in the upper atmosphere. X-ray lasers can be used to create a sudden current surge in the upper atmosphere, which emits a radio-wave pulse to destroy ground-based electronics and communication. An underground nuclear explosion could be used to deliver an enhanced shock wave to a strategic target.[5]

The potential areas for nuclear weapon development are numerous. Third-generation nuclear weapons can be developed to focus aspects of the power of a nuclear explosion for specific purposes in a variety of ways. The significant increase in the variety of military techniques for which nuclear weapons can be developed increases the potential that they *will* be used. The greater effectiveness in using a third-generation nuclear weapon for a particular military mission will similarly significantly increase the likelihood for its use. However, when one side explodes a nuclear weapon, the other side detects only the nuclear explosion, not the purpose of that explosion. Hence the use of a third-generation nuclear weapon for a specific military purpose has as great a potential for leading to a full-scale nuclear war as ordinary nuclear explosions do.

A portion of the SDI funding is devoted to the research and development of the directed-energy class of third-generation nuclear weapons that will be primarily useful for offensive objectives. The expenses of this research and development are relatively small now, but they may grow rapidly if these weapons are utilized in the future, whether for defensive or offensive purposes. In addition to the costs of deploying such weapons, there may be an offensive buildup by the Soviets in response to their production and then possibly an offensive buildup by the United States in response to the Soviet buildup.

If most Americans were asked to dig into their pockets and support the development of a new generation of powerful nuclear weapons with substantial offensive uses that could accelerate the arms race in ways we cannot anticipate, they would reply with a resounding no! Instead, they have often been publicly asked to support a non-nuclear program to develop a defensive shield with the potential to make nuclear weapons obsolete. Initially, this approach was effective. If these new weapons are deployed sometime in the future, they will significantly increase the risk of nuclear war and create new directions for the arms race that will waste many billions of dollars. No one knows when or how it will end.

CHAPTER 10

Strategic Defense and Arms Control Treaties

There are a number of arms control treaties in force between the United States and the Soviet Union that impinge directly or indirectly on the development of a strategic defense. It is important that these treaties be carefully examined for the implications that the development or building of a missile defense will have on them. Before any decision is made to undertake questionable activities with respect to the treaties, an evaluation should be made of the possible consequences of violating them. This is important and necessary, since these treaties have been carefully developed over years of negotiating and have provided us with a degree of nuclear stability.

If the United States disregards the provisions of these treaties, it will encourage the Soviets similarly to break their commitments in those treaties, and vice versa; this will undo decades of progress that we have made toward arms control and disarmament. The nuclear stability that has been achieved by those treaties will then be lost.

The United States and the Soviet Union cannot negotiate meaningful and effective new arms control treaties if either party violates existing treaties. Given the precarious nuclear state of affairs whereby each side has first-strike weapons, antisatellite weapons, and the ability to make a nuclear strike against the other in a short time, such new treaties and agreements are urgently needed. Thus, the violation of existing treaties places in serious jeopardy opportunities for further progress with the negotiation of new treaties. If treaties are violated in developing a strategic defense, it will provide another motivation for accelerating the arms race (in addition to those discussed in Chapters 6 and 8).

The treaties relevant to a strategic defense, as well as other past nuclear arms treaties between the United States and the Soviet Union, have withstood the test of time. The United States has quite rightly criticized the Soviet Union for occasional violations, yet all such violations have been marginally prohibited (on the periphery of what is covered) and have usually been corrected in response to these objections. The United States has also been guilty of some marginal violations. The major and clear provisions of the treaties have been kept, to the mutual benefit of both sides. It is important that provisions regarding a strategic defense are carefully followed as well. There are several major treaties that are relevant to a strategic defense, and these will be surveyed. (A survey of the provisions of all nuclear arms control treaties can be found in Goldblat.)[1]

The 1972 ABM Treaty

The treaty that is most important and directly relevant to missile defenses is the 1972 ABM Treaty (see the text of this treaty in Appendix 16 and the Agreed Interpretations and Unilateral Statements for this treaty in Appendix 17). This treaty was negotiated after the early experimentation by both sides with ballistic-missile defenses, when each side realized that trying to build such a defense was ineffective and easily countered, making it a worthless endeavor. Chapter 6 discussed how many of the same countermeasures conceived at that time for use against an anti–ballistic missile (ABM) system would also be effective against a strategic defense (using modern space technology). The technological developments that led to strategic defense concepts have not changed the basic conditions that made the ABM Treaty desirable.

The United States and the Soviet Union began bilateral negotiations on strategic arms limitations in 1969. The first phase of the negotiations ended in 1972 with the signing of the SALT I and the ABM treaties, and the second phase in 1979 with the signing of the SALT II Treaty. The first-phase treaties were ratified by the Senate, but the second-phase treaty was not. The Reagan administration declared in 1986 that it would no longer honor the limitations of the Salt II Treaty.

The ABM Treaty allowed each side to maintain two ABM defenses: one for the national capital and one for the missile silos of a selected area. The 1974 protocol that followed this treaty reduced the number of allowed defenses to one: either the national capital or one missile field (see the text of this protocol in Appendix 18). The United States was building its one allowed defense to protect an area of missile silos in South Dakota, but it was finally accepted that ABM systems were effectively worthless as a means of protecting the silos. This project was then scrapped over a year after the protocol when $6 billion had already been spent building it.

An ABM system is defined in Article II of the treaty as "a system to counter strategic ballistic missiles or their elements in flight trajectory." This definition clearly includes all systems investigated in SDI for countering missiles. Article II describes ABM systems as currently (1972) consisting of interceptor missiles tested or deployed in an ABM mode, launchers for ABM interceptors, and radars tested or deployed in an ABM mode. The description of ABM systems current at the time of the treaty covers most systems planned for Phase I deployment. The Space-Based Interceptor (SBI), ERIS, and HEDI rockets are all ABM-interceptor missiles, and the ground-based radar that is needed to supplement the HEDI interception is an ABM radar.

The crux of the 1972 ABM Treaty for SDI lies in Article V: "Each party undertakes not to develop, test, or deploy ABM systems or components which are sea-based, air-based, space-based, or mobile land-based. . . ." The rest of the article makes a similar prohibition against ABM launchers capable of launching more than one interceptor missile at a time.

Article V prohibits the development, testing, or deployment of space-based ABM systems or their components. Thus the development and testing of space-based interceptors (homing rockets) planned for Phase I deployment are prohibited, as are orbiting mirror defenses, orbiting chemical lasers, orbiting particle-beam weapons, or Brilliant Pebbles planned for a future defense. To make a national priority out of developing ABM systems clearly violates the spirit if not the letter of the treaty.

The negotiators of the treaty foresaw problems that might arise from gray areas in the treaty and created the Standing Consultative Commission (SCC) as a forum at which treaty interpretations can be brought up. The creation and maintenance of this commission was written into the treaty through Article XIII. That commission serves the specific purpose of helping resolve gray areas of the treaty and resolving any issues related to the treaty. Both the United States and the Soviet Union have representatives on the commission. In questions that the United States brought to the commission on Soviet Union compliance in the 1970s, the Soviet Union ceased the questionable activity or else provided additional information that allayed the United States' concerns.

The Reagan administration had a history of reinterpretations of the ABM Treaty to justify the development and testing that were taking place under SDI, independent of the SCC. Perhaps that is not so surprising since President Reagan was opposed to the ABM Treaty when it was ratified in 1972.[2] Early in the program the Reagan administration introduced the permissive interpretation of the treaty, in which the development and testing of components were said to be allowed by the treaty if they did not have the full power or accuracy needed for countering missiles or were not at a stage of development where they could be used on a defensive system. Supposedly, under these conditions the components are not "in an ABM mode."

The Pentagon claimed in a report issued in 1985 that everything planned for this first research and technology phase would satisfy the ABM Treaty. Former Ambassador Gerard Smith, who was the chief negotiator of the United States under the Nixon administration for the Salt I accords stated that when he read the administration's report, he felt as if he was reading what expert tax lawyers trying to evade the law had written. He believed this evasion was clearly an attempt to prepare for a treaty breakout and considered it to be a breach of contract.[3]

An example of the permissive interpretation occurred during the Delta 180 experiments in September 1986 when two satellites launched by a Delta rocket were rammed into each other. Each satellite had its own rocket, and one satellite homed in on the other while a variety of sensors were used to test detection of the rocket plume and gathered data on the characteristics of the plume at close range. This test was claimed to be allowed by the ABM Treaty since the systems did not have ABM capabilities. Under a strict interpretation of the treaty, it involved testing for developing ABM components. Such testing is in violation of a strict interpretation of the treaty unless it is explicitly carried out for developing a fixed land-based area defense (which the Delta 180 test was not).

The Reagan administration set forth a reinterpretation (the "broad interpretation") of the ABM Treaty in 1985. This interpretation was first proposed in April of 1985 in a paper written by a member of the Reagan administration. That paper claimed that there was a loophole in the treaty permitting strategic defense development if it was based on technology that was not anticipated when the 1972 ABM Treaty was signed. The claim involved Statement D in the Agreed Interpretations (Appendix 17) that were added to the treaty. Abraham Sofaer, a former federal judge who was the legal advisor to the State Department, became a major advocate promoting the new interpretation of the treaty, and Assistant Secretary of Defense Richard Perle became a chief architect of this view. In October of 1985, National Security Adviser Robert McFarlane announced this new view publicly in a televised interview—that developing and testing of exotic technology not contemplated when the treaty was signed is allowed—in an effort to give wide latitude to SDI development within the ABM Treaty.[4]

This claim created a furor by critics of this attempt to redefine the treaty, and President Reagan decided that he "agreed in principle, but not in practice" with the reinterpretation given by Robert McFarlane. A Reagan spokesman said that the president believed that this position was justified and left open the possibility that it could be adopted as U.S. policy sometime in the future. The "broad interpretation" came under rather sharp criticism from our European allies as well as condemnation by the Soviet Union.

Secretary of State George Shultz stated before a NATO assembly a few days later that this "broader interpretation is fully justified," but that SDI will be conducted in accordance with a narrow interpretation of the treaty. The argument for the broad interpretation centers around the Article II definition of ABM systems, followed by "currently consisting of" ABM interceptor missiles, launchers, and radars. The Reagan administration argued that this should be read as "only those consisting of" interceptor missiles, launchers, and radars. Thus the ABM Treaty prohibits only "traditional ABM components" and not exotic systems based on new technology. Statement D of the Agreed Interpretations is then interpreted to amend the treaty to allow for development and testing, but not deployment, of exotic systems in any basing mode (sea, air, space, or land).[5]

Ambassador Gerard Smith headed the team involved in the negotiation of the ABM Treaty in 1971 and 1972. He asked President Nixon at the time about whether the United States should pursue a treaty that included future ABM systems. President Nixon cabled him, noting that the provisions should not prevent the development and testing of future ABM components in the fixed land-based mode. However, neither party should engage in developing, producing, testing, and deploying of sea-based, air-based, space-based, and mobile land-based interceptors, launchers, radars, and components. He stated that "Our objective is to reach agreement on the broad principle that [it] should not be interpreted in such a way that either side could circumvent its provisions through future ABM systems or components. We intend to handle any problems that may arise through the joint commission and the formal review procedures."

The wording of Statement D, added in the Agreed Interpretations, came from the U.S. Joint Chiefs of Staff, who had asked for an exemption to cover fixed land-based laser systems for destroying enemy warheads then under research. The project at that time was top secret, and the purpose of the statement added was to exempt the development of a ground-based laser for a fixed land-based defense without actually mentioning the project by name. The treaty was written to prohibit all ABM systems and components, with the exception of fixed land-based systems, and Agreed Statement D was added to update the treaty for developing and testing a new technology for fixed land-based systems protecting a specific area, as allowed by the treaty.[6]

In March 1987 six former secretaries of defense signed a statement that was sent to the president and key members of Congress. The statement reaffirmed their support for the ABM Treaty and stated that both the United States and the Soviet Union should continue to adhere to the traditional interpretation of the 1972 ABM Treaty. This bipartisan statement was endorsed by Robert McNamara (secretary from 1961–1968), Clark Clifford (1968–1969), Melvin Laird (1969–1973), Elliot Richardson (1973), James Schlesinger (1973–1975), and Harold Brown (1977–1981).[7]

The "broad interpretation" of the 1972 ABM Treaty was scuttled with the enactment of the Biden condition in the Senate on the ratification of the Intermediate Nuclear Forces (INF) Agreement in 1988 (discussed in the next chapter). This condition declared that any interpretation inconsistent with the common understandings at the time of negotiation of the treaty to be invalid (see the wording of the Biden condition for ratification in Appendix 19). In response to this condition on the ratification, President Reagan conveyed a message to the Senate, declaring that he could not "accept the proposition that a condition in a resolution of ratification can alter the allocation of rights and duties under the Constitution." In a response, the chairman of the Foreign Relations Committee, Senator Pell, stated that the condition does not alter the Constitution and is binding, taking effect when the INF Treaty is brought into force.[8]

The SCC is the obvious place to resolve any questions or disagreements on the treaty. It is the forum to resolve questions on U.S. development and testing of SDI. It helped resolve the issue of Soviet phased-array radar in the vicinity of Krasnoyarsk, which was in violation of the treaty. The Soviets stopped construction of this radar in 1987 in response to U.S. concerns that it violated the ABM Treaty. They finally agreed that this radar violated the ABM Treaty in October 1989 and stated that they would remove it. The SCC forum for the treaty is where questions on what the United States and Soviet Union are allowed to do without violating the treaty should be investigated. These proper diplomatic channels have not been effectively used to resolve questions on SDI development and testing, probably because the positions the Reagan administration set forth represented an effort to avoid compliance with the treaty, not to resolve implications of the treaty for the Strategic Defense Initiative. Whether any substantial change in these positions will occur under the Bush administration is an open question.

SDI Tests and the ABM Treaty

Typically two interpretations of the ABM Treaty are used in discussions on development and testing in SDI: the broad interpretation and the traditional interpretation. However, the traditional or narrow interpretation can be broken up into two forms: a restrictive interpretation and a permissive one. The permissive interpretation is the one adopted by the Reagan administration near the beginning of SDI: Development and testing of ABM components is allowed if they are not operating with the capabilities or power levels required for a missile defense. This permissive interpretation is generally the one referred to as a traditional interpretation, while the broad interpretation is the one introduced publicly by Robert McFarlane in October of 1985: ABM systems or components arising from new technologies are not covered by the treaty and can be fully tested (but not deployed).

Five former secretaries of presidential cabinets endorsed a paper sent to Secretary of State Schultz in August of 1986, calling for an agreement with the Soviet Union to delay testing for 10 years. This paper called for a restrictive interpretation of the 1972 ABM Treaty and an adherence to the numerical nuclear weapon limits set by the 1979 Salt II Treaty. The endorsers were Melvin Laird, secretary of defense under President Nixon; James Schlesinger, secretary of defense under Presidents Nixon and Ford, and secretary of energy under President Carter; Brent Scowcroft, national security adviser under President Ford; Harold Brown, secretary of defense under President Carter; and Cyrus Vance, secretary of state under President Carter.[9]

The delay in SDI testing called for by these five former officials was ignored by the Reagan administration. In May 1987 a study by the Pentagon was sent to President Reagan urging adoption of the broad interpretation of the treaty to allow four new tests that violated the traditional interpretation. The report claimed that these tests would reduce development time by at least two years, allowing early deployment in the mid-1990s. The four tests proposed:

1. Tiered Hierarchy Overlay Research (THOR), a series of experiments using space platforms for testing the capability to intercept missiles and dummy warheads with homing rockets that ram into their targets. (The ABM Treaty explicitly states that ABM interceptor missiles cannot be tested, so this test would not even satisfy the broad interpretation.)

2. Interception of a submarine-launched missile with space-based sensors used for tracking and surveillance, and rockets used for interception.

3. Laser Integrated Space Experiment (LISE), testing a space-based chemical laser.

4. Sensor Integrated Discrimination Experiment (SIDE), a test to assess how sensors can function as a network in attempting to distinguish warheads from decoys.[10]

The THOR, LISE, and SIDE experiments were originally planned to occur in 1990 if the broad interpretation was officially adopted. However, they were proposed to encourage the official adoption of the broad interpretation and have been canceled. The SDIO used the broad interpretation in a discussion of its compliance with the ABM Treaty in its 1989 report to Congress. However, in a brief note at the end of that discussion, it claimed that no experiment has been approved that does not fall in the traditional interpretation, primarily because of the Biden condition and the fact that congressional approval is required for any test.[11]

The THOR experiment has been replaced by the two Space-Based Interceptor (SBI) experiments scheduled for 1991, which will make a suborbital interception rather than the actual orbiting platforms of the THOR experiment. These are tests for the space-based components planned for Phase I deployment (described in Chapter 7). In these tests, the SBI will be launched from the test range of Kwajalein (allowed in the treaty), but will use a Minuteman I missile for the latter stage of boosting and will intercept a booster launched from a nearby island. The experiments have been justified under the permissive version of the traditional interpretation but will undermine the ban on space-based testing in the ABM Treaty.[12]

LISE has been replaced by the Zenith Star, a space-based chemical-laser test scheduled for the mid-1990s. This test will use an Alpha laser designed by TRW (which had its first firing test in March 1990), and a LAMP (Large Advanced Mirror Program) mirror designed by Itek. The test will examine pointing, tracking, and firing of the laser in space. This experiment will violate the ABM Treaty if the laser power and mirror capability make it capable of substituting for an ABM interceptor.

A significant number of tests are planned in the next five years for strategic defense systems. In fact, after the first five years of SDI (the research and technology phase), SDI was deemed to enter the test phase. A large number of tests are scheduled for SDI in the early 1990s, the majority of which are designed for deployment of a Phase I defense.[13]

Two major tests for SDI systems that have been made recently are

1. Delta Star Experiment (another in the series using a Delta booster) in March 1989. The major purpose of the test was to test sensors for the identification of rocket plumes from a variety of rockets launched.

Another purpose was to test the durability of materials designed for space-based defense vehicles in a space environment.[14]

2. Beam Experiment Aboard Rocket (BEAR), testing the firing of a neutral beam for possible use in midcourse discrimination, in June 1989. This test was supposed to lay the groundwork for a much larger test in the mid-1990s.[15]

Several other SDI tests are planned for the near future. One of these is the Airborne Optical Adjunct (AOA) test for acquisition, tracking, and discrimination of dummy warheads and decoys from a Boeing 767, scheduled for 1990. The infrared telescopic device is being developed to track missiles in the reentry phase. This test will be followed up by an Airborne Laser Experiment (ALE) in 1991 using a laser range-finder with AOA. In its 1987 report to Congress, SDIO argued that the AOA will not be capable of substituting for ABM components due to its sensor and aircraft limitations. These limitations were not specified since they are classified.

The aircraft limitations are irrelevant to the issue of whether this experiment will violate the ABM Treaty. Boeing 767s have the capability of staying in the air for longer times than would be necessary for countering warheads. The question is whether the sensors on the AOA experiment or its ALE follow-up have the capacity for use in the ABM mode. If the AOA or ALE experiment demonstrates that the AOA device is capable of substituting for an ABM radar, it would be a violation of the ABM Treaty. Thus, if the sensor achieves the planned capability to detect, track, and discriminate warheads from decoys, it would violate Article V and Agreed Statement D as an air-based component capable of substituting for an ABM radar.

A Boost Surveillance and Tracking Satellite (BSTS) is scheduled to be launched from an upgraded Titan 2 rocket for a test in 1992. This is being developed for use in the boost-phase defense. Similarly, a Space-Based Surveillance and Tracking Satellite (SSTS), which is being developed for use in the midcourse defense, will be launched in the mid-1990s. If the sensors of the systems are adequate to guide strategic defense interceptors, they are a violation of the 1972 ABM Treaty.

Other experiments are planned in the near future. These include

1. Laser Atmospheric Compensation Experiment and the Relay Mirror Experiment (LACE/RME) was begun in 1990. The satellite carrying the space equipment will be in orbit for over two years.

2. Exoatmospheric Reentry Interceptor Subsystem (ERIS) will be tested in 1991. This is the midcourse interceptor being developed for Phase I deployment.

3. High Endoatmospheric Interceptor (HEDI) will be tested in 1991. This is a terminal-phase interceptor being developed for early deployment.

4. A 10-megawatt Free-Electron Laser is scheduled to be tested at White Sands in 1991.

5. Space-Based Railgun test is scheduled to be carried out on the shuttle about 1993.

6. Mid-Infrared Advanced Chemical Laser (MIRACL), a moderately high-power excimer laser is planned for testing in 1991.

The interpretation of the ABM Treaty has created a dichotomy between United States and Soviet negotiators. The Soviets have refused to accept the permissive traditional interpretation used by the Reagan administration. An alternative version that has been proposed is the establishment of threshold limits on the performance of devices that can be used in antimissile systems. The thresholds at the time of signing the ABM treaty were applied in Article III, IV, and Agreed Statements B, C, and D. The threshold proposal would apply limits to laser brightness, interceptor height, mirrors and apertures, reactor-core fuel mass, radar deployments, and annual mass launched into orbit.[16]

The LACE/RME test scheduled for 1990 violates the restrictive interpretation of the ABM Treaty as well as proposed limits in the threshold interpretation. The HEDI and free electron laser tests in 1991 will violate the threshold limits, while the MIRACL test in 1991 and the BSTS test in 1992 will violate the restrictive interpretation limits. The Space-Based Interceptor test, the Space-Based Railgun test, and the Zenith Star test will violate both the restrictive and threshold interpretations of the ABM Treaty. Because it is a space-based interceptor with the ability to kill missiles at long range, Zenith Star violates the permissive interpretation of the ABM Treaty and can be allowed only under the broad interpretation of the treaty. Because of its use of space-based missile interceptors similar to the use at the time of the 1972 ABM Treaty, the Space-Based Interceptor test appears to violate even the broad interpretation of the ABM Treaty.

The focus of the testing is the preparation for Phase I deployment systems, with some of the tests being planned for laser systems to provide a second phase after Phase I deployment. The testing schedule has been set up so that Phase I deployment can begin in the late 1990s. Once deployment begins, the United States will have completely withdrawn from the treaty. Even the broad interpretation does not allow deployment.

The 1967 Outer Space Treaty

An important development in the 1960s that was hailed as an important step to ensure peaceful uses of space was the 1967 Treaty of Principle Governing Activities of States in the Exploration of Outer Space (see the text of this treaty in Appendix 20). The purpose of the treaty was to prevent the spread of nuclear weapons to outer space, stating that all mankind had an interest in exploring and using outer space for peaceful purposes. Placing nuclear and mass destruction weapons in space are specifically prohibited by that treaty. It was preceded by the 1963 Partial Test Ban Treaty, which prohibited nuclear testing in the atmosphere or outer space (see the text of that treaty in Appendix 21). One purpose of the 1967 Outer Space Treaty was to strengthen the restrictions made by the Partial Test Ban Treaty because of the developments both sides had made in exploring and using outer space in the interval between the treaties.

Clearly X-ray-laser and nuclear-"shotgun" space weapons are prohibited by both treaties, and it is conceivable that certain laser and particle-beam defensive weapons are prohibited by the 1967 Outer Space Treaty, given their potential for causing mass destruction in space. Early research and development of the X-ray-laser and nuclear-"shotgun" weapons involve underground nuclear explosions, which are consistent with the treaties. Development of the weapons at later stages for a ballistic-missile defense will require testing with nuclear explosions or nuclear debris from explosions in a space environment, which is prohibited by both treaties.

Other Relevant Treaties

The close connection between ballistic-missile defense systems and antisatellite weapons was discussed in Chapter 8. The technology that is developed for countering ballistic missiles will provide much greater capabilities for destroying satellites. If the United States develops defensive systems, both sides will undoubtedly develop more effective antisatellite weapons. Thus treaties addressing antisatellite weapons also have strong implications for missile defense systems.

The 1974 Agreement for the Prevention of Nuclear War prohibits any satellite interference that poses the threat of war (see the text of this treaty in Appendix 22). The reason for this is that the presence of these satellites provides stability by ensuring that the other side does not make surprise attacks or violate mutual treaties. In addition, Salt I, Salt II, and the 1972 ABM Treaty have provisions that prohibit interference with the national technical means of verification, which is primarily provided by satellites.

Systems or technologies that have some capabilities to take out ballistic missiles have an even greater capacity to take out satellites, and having the capability will provide temptation and encouragement to use it when it appears advantageous. The United States cannot develop a missile defense and ensure that the intent of these treaties is kept.

Another treaty that is relevant to SDI is the 1968 Treaty on the Non-Proliferation of Nuclear Weapons, signed by 122 nations, including the United States and the Soviet Union. The nuclear-weapon nations agreed that they would take concrete steps to halt the global buildup in nuclear arms. Furthermore, the treaty forbids the exchange of nuclear technology for military purposes or the cooperation of research to develop such technology between states having nuclear weapons and those that do not.[17] This treaty prohibits any international cooperation on the development of nuclear-weapon technologies for a strategic defense. This would cover, for example, European agreements for cooperation on defense technology (see Chapter 11).

Several treaties have been discussed in this chapter which facets of the SDI program have probably violated or are anticipated to violate with planned future developments. Apparent disregard to honoring these treaties can set back progress in arms control by several years. The only thing such violations can accomplish is a defense that may eventually cost over a trillion dollars and will be more effective in accelerating nuclear arms buildup and decreasing nuclear stability than it is in countering a nuclear attack. What a price for strategic defense!

CHAPTER 11

The Strategic Defense Initiative and European Allies

The Tactical Offer to the Europeans

When SDI was initiated in the United States in 1983, it came as a complete surprise to our North Atlantic Treaty Organization (NATO) allies. They had not received any warning or request for advice on the matter. This created concern on their part because of the impact it could have on the NATO alliance and European security, as well as skepticism as to whether reintroducing strategic defense after it had supposedly been finally abandoned with the 1972 ABM Treaty was a good idea.

The Europeans were initially ignorant of what the new program involved and looked on it as a possible new expansion of the arms race. They were also concerned about the question as to whether it might provide some immunity to the United States against a nuclear arms attack while leaving Europe (which is much closer to the Soviet bloc) just as vulnerable as ever and thus more likely to be a target. Hence, the general European attitude to the program was neutral at best, and it received little European support initially.

In April 1984, Secretary of Defense Weinberger presented the plans under SDI to the NATO defense ministers. After that presentation many defense ministers went public with their disapproval of the plan. For example, Defense Minister Manfred Woerner of West Germany said it could destroy the NATO alliance. This was because a perfect defense cannot be achieved, whereas a partially effective defense would increase the tension and instability between the superpowers, expanding the arms race. The

117

defense minister of France, Claude Cheysson, proclaimed that SDI was trying to create a Maginot Line in space.[1]

One of the concerns of the Reagan administration was receiving support of U.S. allies on the SDI program and even their participation in it. A program was begun to offer attractive contracts to these countries for some of the developments in technology that would have to be made. For example, Germany is well known for its research and development in the area of optics, so it was a logical choice for industrial contracts on optical sensors and mirrors. The new source of money and potential benefits to industrial technology in allied countries would make it more difficult for them to reject cooperation with the United States in this program. After all, the American people would be paying for it, not the allies.

The U.S. government made attempts to persuade the Europeans of the benefits they would receive from SDI. For example, in an address made to the British government and industrial representatives by U.S. Strategic Defense Initiative representatives, it was stated that they should begin to think how they could participate in the proposed ABM system and not assume that the United States had all the answers. One of these SDI spokesmen was Edward Gerry, president of W. J. Schafer Associates. He noted to reporters that five specific complaints had been voiced by Europe so far:[2]

1. A missile defense would increase the likelihood of limited aggression.

2. SDI might degrade the present nuclear deterrence force, which depends on mutually assured destruction.

3. SDI might reduce the credibility of the United States' strategic commitment to NATO.

4. SDI might reduce the likelihood of East-West arms control negotiations.

5. Success of the program might cause future funding for NATO to be reduced.

In March 1985, Secretary of Defense Weinberger addressed the NATO Nuclear Planning Group in Luxembourg, inviting the NATO nations, Israel, Japan, and Australia to participate in SDI research. This offer was given the name of the Tactical Defense Initiative and was put together by the United States for Europe primarily because of the need to give money in return for political support. An intent was to stimulate research by our NATO allies to develop a defense against short- and medium-range missiles in Europe. Despite the general European skepticism about SDI, the potential monetary and technological benefits were hard to turn down.

In testimony given before the Committee on Banking, Finance, and Urban Affairs (Subcommittee on Economic Stabilization) in December 1985, John Pike of the Federation of American Scientists stated that there are several barriers to European participation in SDI. These included provisions of the 1972 ABM Treaty, the limited capabilities of European companies to develop the demanding requirements for a missile defense, the lack of significant commercial benefits in contracts the United States was willing to give to the Europeans, and restrictions that required some of this work to be done in the United States. Aware of some of these barriers, European agreement for participation in the program was linked to the technology transfer restrictions to benefit the participating countries.[3]

In the next section the importance of the 1972 ABM Treaty on European participation will be presented. The responses of several countries to the offer of the United States to participate will be summarized in later sections. The European Defense Initiative will then be analyzed, followed by the recent Intermediate Nuclear Force (INF) agreement, a superior resolution to many efforts for a European defense.

The 1972 ABM Treaty and European Participation

In addition to its importance on the question of the treaty validity of several parts of the SDI program, the 1972 ABM Treaty has restrictions on contracting of ABM systems out to other countries.

Article IX of the treaty states, "To assure the viability and effectiveness of this Treaty, each Party undertakes not to transfer to other States, and not to deploy outside it national territory, ABM systems or their components limited by this treaty." Chapter 10 discussed how a large part of the program is used for ABM component development and testing, part of which is in violation of a strict interpretation of the treaty. If some of this component development is contained in contracts let out to the Europeans on SDI, this would be an additional violation of the treaty.

In the Agreed Interpretations regarding the ABM Treaty, Statement G states that "the Parties understand that Article IX of the Treaty includes the obligation of the US and the USSR not to provide to other States Technical descriptions or blueprints specifically worked for the construction of ABM systems and their components limited by the treaty." A large part of the ABM research and development of the SDI program involves work requiring such blueprints or specifications for the development of such components, and any let out to the Europeans enabling them to fulfill contracts they received under this program would be a violation of the treaty.

The stipulations from the ABM Treaty forbid the transfer of ABM components and the plans for those components, and thus the European participation in a substantial part of the program is prohibited. Thus up to half of the SDI program has been inaccessible to European participation.

The European nations have a strong interest in preserving the ABM Treaty and have all been strong supporters of the treaty since it was written. Leaders in the NATO countries made compliance with that treaty a key condition to participation in the program. Thus even if the United States had chosen to broaden the European participation under conditions forbidden by the treaty, it is rather unlikely that the Europeans would have gone along with it.

The British Response

Britain's first reaction to SDI and the Weinberger speech in April 1984 was rather wary. Even Prime Minister Thatcher had expressed concern about unknown consequences on the movement of the arms race into the space area and did not endorse the program. She saw the American SDI program leading to an expansion that would increase the cost to Great Britain. The Thatcher government had been involved in a debate on a controversial $10-billion project to upgrade its nuclear force with the purchase of American Trident II D-5 missiles. These concerns led to a meeting between President Reagan and Prime Minister Thatcher at Camp David in December 1984.

An invitation was made to Europeans for contracts in 1985. President Reagan and Prime Minister Thatcher agreed on four points in the Memorandum of Understanding about the purpose and limitations of the Strategic Defense Initiative in December 1985, in return for her endorsement of the program:

1. The aim of the program is not to achieve superiority over the Soviet Union but balance with it.
2. The SDI deployment would be a matter of negotiation because of treaty limitations.
3. East-West negotiations should aim at the achievement of security with a reduction of the offensive levels of both sides.
4. The aim is to enhance and not undermine nuclear deterrence.[4]

The broad interpretation of the 1972 ABM Treaty proposed (but not officially adopted) by the Reagan administration in the fall of 1985, the Reagan administration's refusal to open SDI up for negotiation in arms control talks with the Soviet Union, and the move for early deployment each appear to be in contradiction to the second point. Furthermore, Chapters 6 and 8 discussed how the effect of the program runs counter to the last two points. However, with agreement on these points, President Reagan sold Prime Minister Thatcher on the program.

In December 1985 Great Britain was the first European ally to agree to cooperate on SDI. A pledge of support of the United States for Great Britain was made with British Defense Secretary Heseltine. Secretary Heseltine had a negative reaction to the offer made in Secretary Weinberger's address in April 1984. At the time of the British agreement, he had insisted on a guarantee of at least $1.5 billion in support, but the United States rejected that commitment, saying only that the British support would be substantial. At the time of the signing, Secretary of Defense Weinberger made the claim that the SDI program would end the suicide of nuclear deterrence.[5] (The claim is nonsense and contradicts point 4 of the agreement.)

The agreement for cooperation of Great Britain on the U.S. SDI program caused a major split in the British cabinet; a large number of cabinet members were opposed to it. There were at least two reasons for this opposition. One was that offers for work coming from the SDI funding would drain the short supply of skilled scientists and researchers away from other research programs of very high priority. There was particular concern that it would drain away those involved in civilian applications of advanced computing techniques. For example, one high-priority program was the $500-million Alvey program on microelectronic research. A second concern was that agreement did not provide assurance that the United States would not put serious constraints on using the research results obtained by British scientists for non-SDI purposes.[6]

The research on the initiative in Great Britain that would result from cooperation on SDI had little potential application in the commercial world there, except for the computer and microchip technology that would be involved. British contracts on SDI were awarded in particle-beam weapon development, European defense development, electronics, and sonar technology. By the end of 1986, Britain had been awarded $24 million in industrial contracts. This was considerably less than the $1.5 billion that British Defense Secretary Heseltine had requested.[7]

Response of West Germany

The industrial capabilities of West Germany are very relevant to some of the areas where technology development would be needed for SDI. In offers made for cooperation on SDI, the West German officials told their American counterparts that any cooperation on strategic defense research must provide technological gains for Germany as well as the United States.[8]

Hearings on the German response to the offer were held at the Bundestag in December 1985. A group of German arms control experts testified before the parliamentary committee on American cooperation and the proposed development of a European defense and necessary technologies. Conservative members of the committee ruled against taking testimony from U.S. experts because they felt it was a German decision that should not be influenced by American views. Of about fifteen German experts testifying only one clearly favored supporting developing a missile defense.

The Bundestag approved a possible cooperation on the technology transfer. However, the negotiations that were going on between the United States and Germany, which gave the impression that an agreement was close at hand shortly after the British-American agreement on December 6, 1985, hit some snags. The reason for this was that the Kohl government wanted to play down the military implication of its cooperation in the program, while the Pentagon wanted to highlight them. The concern was that the strategic implications of this program could have an adverse effect on the NATO nuclear deterrence policy. Weinberger reached an agreement with the West Germans in the latter part of March 1986, which settled these difficulties.[9]

West Germany agreed to participate with the United States, undertaking contracts for research and development of certain aspects of the SDI project. This possibility of incoming money overrode other concerns that some Germans had expressed. Shortly thereafter, the Soviet Union filed a formal protest on West Germany's move to join the research effort.[10] By the end of 1986, West German firms had been awarded $45 million in contracts.[11]

Other Countries' Reactions to the Tactical Defense Initiative

Unlike Britain and West Germany, the French steadfastly refused to reach an agreement for cooperation on SDI. They were unwilling to engage their industries in the European research on SDI.

However, they softened their approach in late 1985 because of U.S. efforts to gain European support. France has two government-owned electronics and weapons companies that were among the first European enterprises to compete for contracts on SDI. It permitted companies to vie for contracts, although it did not endorse the effort.[12]

As a possible alternative to the European offer of cooperation in SDI research, the French government proposed the creation of Eureka, or European Coordination Agency, in mid-1985 to conduct high-technology scientific research similar to that made possible with SDI, but with an emphasis on civilian uses. The purpose was to band European countries together in their own projects for economic development. Shortly after the Eureka initiative, SDI cooperation had also been turned down by Norway, Denmark, Belgium, and the Netherlands, and Eureka had the potential of bringing those countries into the program. Some support for Eureka and resulting cooperation arose, but the program lacked the organization, financial commitment, and focus that SDI presented. Only the French, German, and Dutch governments committed funds for the program, totaling $385 million. By mid-1986 the program had endorsed 72 projects in areas including robotics, lasers, personal computers, silicon chips, telecommunication, information processing, and transportation.[13]

Sweden realized that the contracts that could come out of their cooperation on the SDI program would be potentially fewer than those of other countries that had agreed to participate. Thus there was not such an overriding concern on the possible financial benefits that could arise from cooperation, and the decision could be made on more rational ground of how well the Swedes supported the Americans in their endeavor.

The Stockholm International Peace Research Institute (SIPRI) in Sweden is devoted to analysis of a number of modern critical problems on nuclear weapons and disarmament, including space weapons and the militarization of space. SIPRI produced an important study that led to subsequent U.S. research showing the occurrence of a nuclear winter after a nuclear war (discussed in the next chapter). It also has made analyses of several undesired consequences of antisatellite and other space weapons. The information undoubtedly had an influence on the Swedish people and government. In early 1986 the Swedish government proclaimed that it wanted no part of cooperation with the United States in SDI development, and joined Norway, Denmark, Belgium, and the Netherlands in refusing cooperation with SDI.

Japan was of particular interest for cooperation on SDI because of the major computer development problems to be solved before building a space missile defense. The United States made a major effort to get Japan's cooperation because of its large industrial base and advances in the computing area. Like France, Japan also refused to cooperate with the United States on SDI for more than a year after it had begun studying the question and engaging in serious talks with the United States on participation. This was despite some urging from Secretary of Defense Weinberger and other defense officials.[14]

In September 1986 the Japanese allowed for the possible involvement of their government and industry research agencies in the program. But at that time they stopped short of guaranteeing Japanese participation in the program, indicating that there would be no encouragement or discouragement for participation of the research agencies that were allowed to participate. That was left open and seemed to hinge on commercial benefits the Japanese could expect.[15] In July 1987, after several months of negotiations, Secretary Weinberger and Ambassador Matsunaga of Japan signed an agreement for Japanese industrial participation in SDI.

The European Defense Initiative

Support in Europe grew in late 1985 for the European Defense Initiative (EDI), introduced by German Defense Minister Woerner for the development of European defenses to Soviet threats that were not covered by SDI but would provide European benefits for research developed under SDI. The objective of the initiative was for the European nations to band together for a strictly European version of a missile defense that will be used to protect the European continent against the shorter-range Soviet ballistic missiles SS-21, SS-22, SS-23, as well as bombers and cruise missiles. Developments under SDI could not help the threat to NATO forces, but SDI applications might benefit European defenses by upgrading their technology and helping deploy upgraded weapons. Four categories that were considered to fall under such a program:[16]

1. Upgraded surface-to-air missiles. Systems capable of attacking aircraft would be developed to be capable also of shooting down missiles.
2. Laser beams and kinetic-energy weapons.
3. Satellite systems for remote sensing that could acquire data on the incoming missiles necessary to target them.
4. Advanced communication, command, and control technologies (capabilities always necessary for military operations in a battle).

The discussion in previous chapters of the difficulties of using defensive laser-beam and kinetic-energy weapons applies to shorter-range missiles and weapons since there will always be ways for the Soviets to foil and counter them, even if effective weapons are developed. The advantage of a defense against tactical missiles is that the missiles are slower, making them easier to intercept. However, there is greater difficulty in intercepting shorter-range missiles and other weapons that do not go nearly as far out into space. The shortness of the flight path and time available to respond restricts the defense to the terminal phase.

The principal effort under EDI focused on surface-to-air Anti-Tactical Ballistic Missiles (ATBMs). A motivation for developing these missiles was presented in the 1983 Hoffman study for the Pentagon, which recommended proceeding rapidly with the deployment of partially effective anti-missile systems. It argued that such a program would reduce anxieties of our allies about weakening U.S. commitments to European defense with SDI. It also pointed out that the development of ATBMs was consistent with the ABM Treaty but that the developments on ATBMs might later be useful for a terminal-phase defense under SDI.[17]

A European motivation for the ATBM was the fear that the Warsaw Pact might use the recently deployed Soviet SS-21 and SS-23 missiles, which were highly accurate and might have been used as a preemptive strike against NATO. The only response available to the NATO defenses would have been to rely on the threat of nuclear retaliation to deter a Soviet attack. Having ATBMs was seen as a way to counter this threat without relying on a more ominous threat.

Congressional supporters of SDI, particularly Senator Dan Quayle (now vice-president) and Representative Duncan Hunter, urged in late 1985 and 1986 that ATBMs should be deployed as soon as available, seeing them as a means of institutionalizing SDI while President Reagan was still in office. Two new types of missiles proposed at that time for the European ATBM system were the HEDI missiles (discussed in Chapter 7) and Terminal Imaging Radar (TIR) sensor. Yet these are components of an ABM system. Article IX of the ABM Treaty prohibits the transfer ABM systems or components to other states, or deployment outside the United States and the Soviet Union.[18]

Penetration aids, such as missile decoys, used along with the launch of tactical ballistic missiles that ATBMs would be designed to counter are much simpler and more efficient than with strategic missiles. Decoys do not burn up on reentry because the velocity is slower, and thus survive until they hit the ground. Decoys are more difficult to distinguish from tactical ballistic missiles on radar than they are in the terminal defense against strategic missiles. Furthermore, it is easier and cheaper to use radar jammers with tactical ballistic missiles than with strategic missiles.[19]

The estimated cost of around $50 billion for the building of ATBMs implied it would be cost-effective for the Warsaw Pact to build up their offensive weapons in response. However, the INF agreement in late 1987 put restrictions on the Soviet missiles that initiated the EDI. Developments under the EDI had the potential of being similar to the mistake that SDI is. It would have been an expensive investment with little useful return and could have been destabilizing to arms control and disarmament in Europe.

The Intermediate Nuclear Forces Agreement

When the U.S. moved to phased deployment of a strategic defense with the first phase planned in the 1990s, there was again a strong reaction from many European quarters. Despite the lucrative contracts that were awarded in the European community under the Tactical Defense Initiative, the uncertain future that an early deployment of SDI would create for the NATO countries was of widespread concern.

A U.S. delegation that included the arms control head Paul Nitze and Assistant Secretary of Defense Richard Perle met with British Prime Minister Thatcher and Foreign Secretary Sir Geoffrey Howe in February of 1987. This occurred just before the U.S.-Soviet arms control talks in Geneva. The U.S. delegation assured Prime Minister Thatcher and Secretary Howe that early deployment under SDI was not planned.[20] This assurance was in contradiction to Secretary of Defense Weinberger's support of early deployment a few weeks earlier, as well as budget shifts under SDI that put more emphasis on the development of systems for a first-phase defense.

The U.S. delegation also met with West German Prime Minister Helmut Kohl, giving him similar reassurances. Prime Minister Kohl insisted that the United States adhere to the provisions of the ABM Treaty, which the European allies supported and the U.S. government had repeatedly assured them it would do.

Plans for development and eventual deployment of a strategic defense under SDI was a major bottleneck in arms control negotiations during the Reagan administration. The summit meetings in 1985 and 1986 failed to produce results because of President Reagan's determination not to compromise on SDI, and Premier Gorbachev's view of a strategic defense as a threatening development in the arms race. It was also a major stumbling block in the Geneva negotiation in 1987.

However, the Soviets had earlier proposed a separation of arms control negotiations on strategic weapons, on which there was an impasse, and medium- to short-range missiles in the European theater. At first the Reagan administration did not accept this separation, possibly because they viewed SDI and a defense for NATO to be linked. However, this separation eventually led to the INF Agreement.

In December of 1987 President Reagan and Premier Gorbachev signed the INF Agreement, which banned production and testing of ground-launched missiles with ranges between 300 and 3,400 miles. It also called for the destruction of existing intermediate-range missiles. This included 1,752 Soviet missiles and 859 U.S. missiles. A few citizen groups campaigned against ratification, but the major opposition to the treaty in the Senate came from Senators Wallop and Helms. The Senate ratified the treaty in May 1988 by a 93–5 vote.[21]

Provisions of the INF Treaty required the elimination of all U.S. and Soviet ground-launched missiles with ranges between 1,000 and 5,500 kilometers (600 to 3,400 miles) within 3 years. Missiles falling into that category are the U.S. Pershing II and Ground-Launched Cruise Missiles, and the Soviet SS-4, SS-5, SS-20, and SSCX-4 missiles. It required the removal within 18 months of all missiles having a range between 500 and 1,000 kilometers (300 to 600 miles). This would include the U.S. Pershing 1a and the Soviet SS-12 and SS-23 missiles, as well as U.S. nuclear warheads for West German Pershing 1s. The treaty also had a number of provisions for procedures in the dismantling of the missiles and their launchers, as well as inspections and verification to ensure compliance by the two parties.

The Soviet Union and the United States began destroying and dismantling their missiles in August of 1988. The removal is scheduled to be completed by the summer of 1991. The treaty is definitely a favorable alternative to the buildup of missiles and antimissiles in that area. It saves the incredible expense that such a buildup would entail and helps prevent the potential disaster that an exchange of missiles would create. Recent major political changes in all Warsaw Pact countries have virtually eliminated the potential for a confrontation between NATO and Warsaw Pact forces that has existed for 40 years. It leads one to hope that the nuclear standoff between the United States and Soviet Union that has existed for 40 years can similarly be finally resolved.

Space Weapons in the Economy, Nuclear War, and Disarmament

A strategic defense will affect the nation's economy as well as nuclear stability and the likelihood of an accidental nuclear war. The nuclear winter studies of a few years ago have implications for a strategic defense. These will be reviewed, along with an examination of possible alternative routes to ending the nuclear arms race (the initially declared goal of SDI), and some final notes.

Economic Implications of a Strategic Defense

An effective strategic defense requires very complex high-technology systems that will require the development of some technologies that will not be viable until well into the future. Developing and deploying an adequate strategic defense requires a long-range program the magnitude of which dwarfs the Manhattan and Apollo projects. If it can be developed, it will require huge monetary outlays, the involvement of a large number of scientists and engineers, major revolutions in computer science, and major advances in the development of large power sources, effective kill mechanisms for future missiles, and invulnerable means of tracking and communication.

The cost to the United States for a full layered ballistic-missile defense will be on the order of $1 trillion or more. Clearly this represents an extraordinary burden on the taxpayers (several thousand dollars per man, woman, and child in the United States). Much better use could be made of such an extraordinarily large sum of money, to do greater good for humanity and to reduce the national debt.

Research and development funds necessary for an advanced-phase strategic defense will substantially increase the disproportionate amount of research and development dollars used for defensive uses over other civilian uses, and this ratio has already increased by an alarming rate during the eighties. In addition, the large buildup in the national debt that occurred during the Reagan administration can be magnified with a program to deploy a strategic defense.

Sophisticated military weaponry using modern technology in the nuclear age has always been expensive, although the technological sophistication and expense of an effective strategic defense exceeds that of any previous weapon system. As an example, one can examine the trade-offs one has for the costs of military weaponry in general and the costs for other worthwhile programs. Just for the cost of one B-2 bomber, some 25,000 tractors could be purchased. If the same amount of money was placed in a useful program, it could be used overseas to combat hunger and starvation that is taking place in certain areas of the world. A summary of some of these trade-offs is presented in Table 12.1.

An interesting fact, evident from Table 12.1, is that if the United States and the Soviet Union could reach an agreement to each devote half of their military defense spending to education and health care in developing countries, it would equal the current expenditures for all 3.6 billion people in these countries. For several reasons, such an agreement is very unlikely: The United States has a $3 trillion national debt that is increasing, and the Soviet Union is spending a very large proportion (about 13%) of its gross national product on the military. Both countries need to reduce defense spending for the sake of their own economies. However, any bilateral agreement to spend a small fraction of cuts from defense spending resulting from bilateral weapon-reduction agreements could be a big boost for education and health in developing countries.

The large proportion of the federal budget that is devoted to military expenditures, which will rise if a decision is made to deploy a strategic defense, has an impact on scientific and technological development in this country. This was apparent with the rapid rise in military spending in the early 1980s. In 1980, 55% of the scientists and engineers in the United States were engaged in military research and development, while the other 45% were involved in research and development in the civilian sector. By 1985, 76% of scientists and engineers were involved in military research and development. This change occurred because the funding of many military research and development programs grew rapidly, while research and development in similar civilian programs was held to a very low

Table 12.1. Trade-offs between military costs and civilian costs

Military Uses	Cost	Civilian Uses
1 F-14 plane	$ 50 million	Annual U.S. child-abuse program
1 B-2 bomber	$500 million	25,000 farm tractors
1 Trident submarine	$ 1.5 billion	Annual education budget for 60 million schoolchildren in 23 developing countries
U.S. Air Force total budget	$ 95 billion	Education budget for 1.2 billion children in Africa, Latin America, and Asia (Japan excluded)
U.S. or USSR total military budget	$300 billion	Total budget of developing countries for education and health care covering 3.6 billion people

Source: Some of these numbers are from annual issues of *World Military and Social Expenditures* (Washington, D.C.: World Priorities).

growth rate and even decreased one year.

With the Strategic Defense Initiative, funding became available for research and development on space weapons, along with studies for strategy and architecture. Large contracts were awarded to companies and national laboratories for developing particular facets of a strategic defense. SDI gained considerable support from scientists and engineers who benefited from research funding from these contracts, even though many of the same scientists and engineers did not see an effective strategic defense as realistically possible. The program provided a source of funding for good scientific research and development in certain areas: computer software development, optical detection and processing, powerful lasers, space maneuvering capabilities, and so on. Thus even some who have supported the program are anything but believers in the ultimate viability of a strategic defense.

Scientists and engineers employed at national laboratories or companies receiving SDI contracts who personally do not support the program are rarely in an environment where they can freely express their criticisms. They often try to avoid getting involved with programs that they do not fully support to sidestep any conflict. That is partly because such scientists know this is a major monetary source of scientific and engineering research and development, and it would be unwise to criticize a program that provides major benefits to the laboratory or company. One example of possible adverse effects that could result from speaking out is the case of Roy Woodruff, of the Lawrence Livermore Laboratory, who spoke out on the technically incorrect claims that were a major motivation for the Strategic Defense Initiative. He was awarded with isolation and a demotion, although that was eventually rectified.

The fact that nonsupporters of the program often try to avoid working on the scientific research at research centers results in a natural bias of those engaged in research supported by SDI. The initial goal of the research and technology phase of SDI was to try to make a scientific decision as to whether we should go ahead with development and deployment of a strategic defense. This bias was likely to be just as important as scientific evaluation in such a decision. The goal of a decision at the end of the first phase was modified with the shift toward an early first-phase deployment in early 1987. The shift implied that the SDIO had already made the decision before the research and technology phase had been completed.

To garner support for the SDI program in colleges and universities, as well as to gain the benefits of widespread research on various areas of science and engineering relevant to developing a strategic defense, the SDIO granted a package of $100 million to support university research in

1985. The package was particularly attractive because many colleges and universities had been hit with budget cutbacks in education and research. As a counter to this effort by the SDIO, a national movement began to get scientists critical of the SDI program to sign a pledge not to work on any aspect of the program's research.

It was interesting that in 1986 Under Secretary for Defense Research and Engineering Donald Hicks made verbal attacks against SDI skeptics, stating that they should not receive any money for research that was currently being funded by the program. He said that he was particularly upset about computer scientists who depended in part on DOD support but voiced skepticism about the feasibility of creating the software demanded by a comprehensive missile defense. When asked about the issue of scientific freedom, Hicks said that freedom works both ways: Professors that are critical are free to keep their mouth shut, and he is free not to give them any money!

The view expressed by Donald Hicks conflicted with the original purpose of the first (research and technology) phase for scientific research and development: to determine whether we should go ahead and build the system. In addition to developments necessary to determine what is possible and achievable, thorough analyses are necessary on what is not feasible, given reasonable forecasts of technology, realistic estimates of the costs involved, and the ease of opponents countering it. If the view of Hicks was made policy, it would preclude scientific objectivity in SDI research, helping to ensure that the decision to deploy a strategic defense will be made. If only supporters are allowed to work for the program, no one would give needed dissemination of scientific results unless they are positive and supportive of the program, and all flaws and potential flaws would be covered up. Such an attitude by any science manager would reveal an interest in removing all scientific objectivity from research.[1]

Development and deployment of the phases of a strategic defense will require an overwhelming portion of this country's resources, and there is no possible guarantee that all of the technologies will be developed or that an effective defense can be constructed and deployed. The evidence from analyzing all aspects on the prospects of such systems appears to indicate that it cannot.

Nuclear Stability and Accidental Nuclear War

Defensive systems planned by the SDIO will be destabilizing to the international arms situation. Phased deployment of a strategic defense will tend to accelerate the arms race both in space and on the ground, which would cost this country more than the huge sums that will be initially spent for building and deploying the phases of defense. There are at least four reasons that this will be the case. The first reason is that the cost of defense is generally much greater than that of the offense that it is designed to counter. Sample calculations imply that the defense could easily cost 10 to 20 times that of the offense it is designed to destroy. Thus the defense could be beaten monetarily with an offensive buildup.

The second reason is that this offensive buildup would concentrate in areas where the defense is the weakest or most vulnerable, such as clustered inexpensive single warhead ICBMs, shorter-range SLBMs, cruise missiles, and bombers. Even if an effective strategic defense could be deployed, the offensive buildup in areas where the defense is less effective or ineffective would after a short period of time make us as vulnerable to Soviet offenses as before, despite the fact that the United States had spent a large amount of money to counter the offense!

The third reason is the offensive capabilities resulting from development and testing of strategic defense. This includes capabilities for anti-satellite use as well as perceived threats of preemptive first-strike use in conjunction with counterforce missile systems (Chapter 8). Offensive capabilities will become available before the defense capabilities can be developed. Offensive uses and perceptions of these uses will seriously decrease the international nuclear stability. The natural response to that new threat will be a Soviet buildup of offensive forces.

The fourth reason is that testing and deploying a strategic defense violates several arms control treaties between the United States and the Soviet Union, particularly the 1972 ABM Treaty and the Agreed Statements arising from that treaty. If the United States violates existing arms control treaties, the Soviets will respond with their own violations. Thus the limitations that these treaties provide on the arms race buildup will be nullified, and an arms race acceleration will naturally result. The United States cannot reasonably hope to negotiate agreements with the Soviet Union to slow and stop the nuclear arms race if we violate existing ones (and vice versa).

President Reagan originally proposed the Strategic Defense Initiative as a potential way to stop the arms race. In fact, because of these four basic reasons it would most likely lead to a major arms race with the Soviets. The United States would monetarily lose that race if it chooses to make a commitment to defensive weapons and the Soviets concentrate instead on the buildup of offensive forces.

The strategic defense effect on the arms race has implications for the idea of a defensive transition that SDI might make possible. The argument for a defensive transition is that if a strategic defense can be deployed that is sufficiently effective (the effectiveness typically referred to is 80%), it will encourage the opponents to make a transition to a defense-dominated buildup, whereas a less effective defense may encourage an offense-dominated buildup. The fallacy of this argument is that it assumes a sudden deployment of a highly effective strategic defense before the Soviets make a response.

The process of building and transporting systems to space once a decision to deploy the strategic defense has been made will be a lengthy process, taking several years. This will allow the Soviets to respond by installing countermeasures on their missiles and building extra offensive forces. Furthermore, its effectiveness in countering the Soviet offensive forces will not be known before it is put to a real test, and this uncertainty will increase the instability and tension, encouraging the Soviets to increase their strategic arms.

The deployment of a first-phase defense in the early twenty-first century will even further invalidate the possibility of a defensive transition. The first-phase defense will not approach the accuracy assumed necessary for the defensive transition and will provide the Soviets more time to develop countermeasures and make an offensive buildup before the second phase is deployed. The same condition holds for the Brilliant Pebbles concept, which is estimated by the originators of the idea to provide a 30% accurate boost-phase defense. It would similarly stimulate the Soviets to develop countermeasures and make appropriate buildups.

In addition to the instability created by strategic defense, the ASATs that both sides will naturally develop along with it will further degrade the nuclear stability. Yet threatened satellites are vital for providing vital information on the other side and will become absolutely essential in case a crisis develops between the United States and the Soviet Union. Decisions must be made quickly upon a warning of a possible nuclear attack by the other side, and if the information needed for verification cannot be obtained because of ASAT attack on vital systems, a wrong decision could easily be made under pressure.

An example of a tragically wrong decision made under pressure because of limited information occurred in the KAL-747 disaster in 1983. This was the case of a Boeing 747 filled with 269 passengers traveling from Alaska to Seoul, South Korea. The Korean pilot had strayed off course, causing the plane to pass over Soviet territory at a time of secret military tests. A Soviet airbase was tracking an American spy plane flying in a circular path out in the Pacific, whose purpose was to observe those tests. The Soviets' radar could cover only part of the flight path, and the plane disappeared off their radar screen. The Soviets did not know it, but the spy plane left the area after that disappearance. However, the stray 747 reappeared from approximately the same location shortly afterward. The Soviet airbase thought they were still tracking the spy plane.[2]

The Soviet airbase went into a frenzy when the plane went over Soviet territory. Military planes were sent up to confront it. Orders were sent to identify it first. A pilot on the military planes reported the strobe light on the plane, but when they pulled up to identify it, the plane made a change of course. This was reported as evasive action, which, combined with the fact that the unidentified 747 was almost into international waters, led to an order to destroy it.

If the Soviets had the essential information that this was a 747 with civilian passengers, they would not have fired at it. The inadequate information, short time available for decision, and pressure led to a decision that caused the tragedy. Yet the military in the United States can be as susceptible to such errors in a critical decision as the Soviet military if vital information is not available. The only thing that can prevent a tragic mistake that could lead to an accidental nuclear war is having access to essential information to make decisions in a time of crisis. Putting up weapons that increase nuclear instability and deploying weapons with the capability to destroy satellites that will provide essential information in a crisis will substantially increase the likelihood of an accidental nuclear war.

Strategic Defense and the Nuclear Winter

In late 1983 some new results appeared on the likely long-term effects of a major nuclear exchange between the United States and the Soviet Union. These came from an analysis of the effects of smoke and dust produced by the nuclear explosions. In this study it was found that the smoke from very hot large-scale industrial fires produced by nuclear airburst attacks on major cities could rise up through the troposphere into the stratosphere. These are the lowest two layers of the Earth's atmosphere. The troposphere occupies the first 5–7 miles above the Earth's surface, and the temperature falls with height in the layer. The stratosphere is the layer above that, extending up to 30 miles' altitude, and is distinguished from the trophosphere by having a temperature inversion—temperature increases with height.

If a forest fire occurs, the smoke rises in the troposphere and cools because of the decreasing temperature with height. It settles and is generally rained out within about a week. However, the very hot smoke produced by a large industrial conflagration created by a nuclear blast is so hot that it would not cool rapidly enough to settle in the troposphere. It would rise up into the stratosphere and because of the inversion, continue to rise until it reached a stagnation region called the ozone layer. That is the region on top of the stratosphere at which the temperature begins decreasing with height again. Here trapping occurs because substances above are cooled and descend, whereas substances below are heated and rise. The ozone trapped in this layer plays an important role in shielding life on Earth from the most dangerous ultraviolet rays.

When smoke from the industrial fires settles in the ozone layer after nuclear detonations, it will strongly absorb the infrared rays from the Sun that are responsible for heating the Earth's surface. The amount of smoke that will end up in this layer has been calculated to be sufficiently large to cause catastrophic decreases in temperatures worldwide. Dust that is generated by ground bursts involved in counterforce strikes will likely also rise to this level and contribute to the blocking of the Sun's heat rays.

The result is the "nuclear winter," which may last a year or more. The original nuclear winter studies predicted that the temperatures will drop low enough to kill most plant life, especially in the tropics, and most animal life. Survivors of the nuclear exchange would then be beset by severe problems of extreme cold, devastation of shelter, starvation, and exposure to radiation and fallout. These conditions could lead to a destruction of over 99% of the population worldwide. Later studies of this phenomenon predict that the effects of the nuclear winter may not be as severe but show only minor qualitative differences.[3]

One of the results of the nuclear winter studies is that the catastrophic results are rather insensitive to the amount of megatons exploded if that lies in the range of 250 megatons to 5,000 megatons. The 10,000 megaton exchange case is only marginally worse. Furthermore, the threshold for the onset of the nuclear winter has been estimated to be as low as 100 megatons. Thus the case of a highly effective strategic defense against a major nuclear attack discussed in Chapter 8, which would still let 800 warheads through, well exceeds the strength of the nuclear explosions that would lead to the nuclear winter and a high rate of destruction of the population in the long run.

The presence of an effective strategic defense in the case of an all-out nuclear exchange does not even prevent nuclear winter, assuming such a defense could be deployed. The long-term result will be equally devastating, whether or not the strategic defense exists.

A Positive Agenda for Nuclear Disarmament

The Strategic Defense Initiative began as a program for research and development on strategic defense to "make nuclear weapons obsolete," as a means of protecting the population of the United States. However, this goal is clearly not possible because of the unreliability of battle-management software, relatively inexpensive counter-measures, inherent leakage, nuclear instability, and the long-term effects of radiation and nuclear winter from the aftermath of any nuclear confrontation. Even if a defense could be made effective against ICBMs, it would be considerably less effective against the shorter-flight SLBMs whose point of launching is not known ahead of time, and relatively ineffective against bombers, cruise missiles, and tactical nuclear weapons. Views of strategic defense as a potential way to defend populations, or as a road to nuclear disarmament, are wrong.

Major advances are needed in the area of disarmament agreements involving space and nuclear weapons developments in the United States and the Soviet Union. Because of the inherent instability created by ASATs, the United States and the Soviet Union need to negotiate an ASAT treaty immediately, prohibiting testing, production, and deployment of these weapons. Provisions of the treaty should provide adequate means for verification of the treaty. An early draft of such a treaty was put forth by the Union of Concerned Scientists.[4]

The two powers should reaffirm and strengthen the 1972 ABM Treaty by adding a protocol or agreed statement to include strategic defense systems based on new technologies explicitly, except for ground-based protection of a missile silo field allowed by the treaty. The Soviets are involved in research on laser weapons as well, so the treaty would benefit both sides. It would also help to negotiate limitations on counterforce ("first-strike") weapons to avoid the instability that has arisen by their development.

An important problem is finding a way to avoid an accidental nuclear war. Although one of the justifications for strategic defense is for preventing accidental nuclear war, that is clearly a two-edged sword. The offensive capabilities of a strategic defense are destabilizing and can be a primary cause of an accidental nuclear launch as well, probably more effectively than it can defend against one. The ALPS proposal avoids creating instability, but there is no assurance that it can neutralize an accidental launch. ALPS is less expensive than a strategic defense, but there may be means of achieving a more effective prevention at a cost similar to or less than ALPS.

A technique that has been recommended in recent years is for an agreement for installing disabling devices on each strategic missile. These disabling devices would be activated by individual secret codes, with the secret codes being determined and classified by the country owning the missile. The criticism is that determining the codes by the opposite side might be a way to disarm the other side. However, that could be avoided by keeping the classified information on the codes separated (there will be over 1,000 such codes) and possibly leaving the less-threatening missiles without a disabling device.

Investigating techniques for preventing an accidental nuclear launch should be a defense priority. Clearly there are better alternatives to this problem than strategic defense, which has been given a major focus for several years now.

The Strategic Defense Initiative was put forth at about the time that the popularity in the United States for a nuclear freeze was near a peak. At that time polls showed that 75% of the American people supported the proposal for stopping the arms by a freeze on the development, deployment, and production of nuclear weapons. The Reagan administration was on record as opposing the freeze. Thus it was convenient to latch onto the idea of a space-based missile defense as a better way not only to end the arms race but also to achieve disarmament.

President Reagan persuaded many in the general public to believe that we could end the nuclear threat rather than achieving stopgap measures to halt the buildup. By taking people's minds off one way to stop nuclear arms buildup, he avoided the loss of his own popularity that might result from the popularity of the freeze he opposed. This occurred despite the fact that there was no prospect of his administration's achieving any arms control agreements at that time.

Arms control treaties that have been negotiated in the last 40 years have slowed the buildup of nuclear arms in important areas, but none has led to a halt or decrease in nuclear arms buildup. Despite the arms control treaties, the nuclear arms race has continued at a fairly rapid rate, so that both the United States and the Soviet Union have built up an immense number of nuclear weapons in the last 45 years. This buildup will continue well into the future unless it is stopped, and a strategic defense will not accomplish this. The nuclear freeze was proposed as a positive first step toward true disarmament — stopping any kind of buildup and allowing actual reductions to be negotiated from there. By banning development, production, and deployment, the present monitoring that each side makes on the other would ensure that any attempt to cheat would be detected.[5]

One can easily compare not only the greater progress in arms control and nuclear stability that could have been made with the nuclear freeze over strategic defense but also the differences in costs. Whereas the cost of developing and deploying a strategic defense that can be countered by countermeasure developments and offensive buildup by the Soviets would run into the hundreds of billions, a nuclear freeze would actually save money on public expenditures by cutting all new nuclear weapon production and deployment.

The proposal for a comprehensive test ban could contribute significantly to long-term stability. The reason is that without the development and testing of nuclear weapons, new ones cannot be developed and deployed. The nuclear test ban would stop the development of dangerous new first-strike missiles in both the United States and the Soviet Union and would reduce fears on each side that the other side is developing the ability to carry out a disarming first strike. It would substantially reduce the risk of a nuclear war.[6]

The reliability of the first-strike weapons each side already has will slowly decrease in time, as will the fear of a first-strike by the other side. Current accuracy in satellite reconnaissance, seismic instruments, and other verification measures would provide highly reliable verifications for such a test ban.[7] Furthermore, with the total test ban, the radioactive pollution of the environment that results from nuclear explosions can be halted for good.

A chance for a test ban treaty existed when the Soviet Union declared a moratorium on nuclear testing in 1985, which was intended to encourage the United States to join them and reach an agreement to prohibit such testing. (A positive example of such a moratorium was set by the United States in the early 1960s, when the Kennedy administration declared a moratorium on nuclear testing, which resulted in the Partial Test Ban in 1963.) The United States never joined in that moratorium or offered to negotiate the agreement, and the Soviet Union began testing again in 1987.

Specific recommendations for nuclear arms control negotiations were set out by a study group at the Center for International Security at Stanford University. These include steps for negotiations and agreements for the Threshold and Limited Test Ban treaties, resolution for agreements in the SSC on ABM Treaty resolutions, agreements for permitted early-warning radars and Soviet dismantling of the radar near Krasnoyarsk (the Soviets have since agreed to dismantle it), and U.S. and Soviet adherence to the Salt I and II agreements.[8]

An agreement for stopping the arms race can also arise from the START talks for a 50% reduction in nuclear arms. A good agreement of this nature could go further than a nuclear freeze if it is accompanied by a nuclear test ban. Not only will such a combined agreement save on the costs of the arms race, unlike the exorbitant costs of strategic defense phases, but will lead to long-term stability against a nuclear war, in contrast to the significantly increased instability in the nuclear threat created with strategic defense.

Closing Comments

In Isaac Asimov's famous science-fiction novel *Foundation Trilogy* there is the interesting remark that humanity had never planned more than a million years into the future. However, the history of the arms race has shown that the United States and the Soviet Union have never planned a decade into the future with a complete evaluation of the consequences of their actions in the nuclear arms arena.

When the atomic bomb was developed, only a few seriously considered what the consequences after the war would be. When the decision was made on the development of the hydrogen bomb, the Oppenheimer committee recommended against an all-out effort for its development because they realized that it would produce a major acceleration in the arms race. The notes from the Oppenheimer committee, declassified after 25 years, were analyzed by Herbert York, who concluded that the committee made the correct recommendation.[9] However, the decision was made for an all-out development, and this helped accelerate the arms race in the 1950s and 1960s. Oppenheimer was subsequently denied his security clearance, in large part because of this recommendation.

In the early 1970s, the United States took the lead in the MIRVing of missiles, and the Soviets followed suit in a few years. Because the Soviets were MIRVing their land-based missiles and developing more accurate warheads, a concern developed in the late 1970s over the potential of the Soviets' being able to destroy our land-based system in a preemptive first strike by multiple targeting our silos. This provided a motivation for the MX missile.

Proponents see strategic defense as a way to protect our missile silos from counterforce weapons the Soviets are developing, yet many in the Soviet Union still fear that the United States will use strategic defense technology in an offensive capacity. The Soviets are very likely to counter any strategic defense deployment by an offensive buildup, which they can do more economically. Thus the SDI program was a major stumbling block to significant disarmament agreements in the summits between President Reagan and Premier Gorbachev. The nuclear arms race continues. But where will it finally end? With a nuclear war?

Early claims that a strategic defense is needed as a way of defending populations, on the other hand, were necessary to garner support for these systems, because it would have been considerably more difficult to convince the American people to accept a major commitment to help protect real or imagined vulnerabilities of land-based missiles. However, as a possible means to protect people from the threat of nuclear war, many citizens of this country supported it. SDI started with this proclaimed goal at a time when the United States was involved in a significant military buildup and the national debt was increasing at a substantial rate.

The military budget is about $300 billion, a 100% increase since 1980. Meanwhile, the United States is running $200 billion annual deficits (closer to $300 billion when the social security profit is subtracted from the budget), the accumulation of which has increased the total U.S. deficit from under $1 trillion to $3 trillion in the last decade. The last thing we need is an expensive new space weapon system that at best can be only temporarily effective and will tend to accelerate the arms race. It will usurp an excessive portion of our country's economic and scientific resources, which could be devoted to much more useful purposes.

The claim that strategic defense might provide a way of rendering nuclear weapons inoperative has successfully detracted from more realistic and much less costly approaches toward stopping the nuclear arms race and achieving key disarmament treaties. If strategic defense is deployed in phases, it will help ensure an arms race for years to come, seriously destabilizing the present international nuclear situation.

Instead of a road to peace and disarmament, deploying a phased strategic defense is a potential road to economic debilitation and even nuclear instability for this country. The United States should halt the buildup in space weapons and concentrate on effective ways to stabilize, minimize, and eventually eliminate the nuclear threat. The United States, the Soviet Union, and other countries with nuclear weapons cannot continue to build nuclear arms and expect they will never be used. Unless we stop the nuclear arms race and make true progress in nuclear disarmament, at some point in the future we may be engaged in a nuclear war and suffer its devastating consequences. The choice is ultimately ours.

Epilogue

Brilliant Pebbles and Phase I Defense

In January 1990 the SDIO made another change in the planned Phase I defense. Recall the shift of strategic defense development to a phased defense with possible early deployment of Phase I that occurred in 1987 (described in Chapter 7). This change in early 1990 was to substitute Brilliant Pebbles (introduced in Chapter 7) for the Space-Based Interceptors (SBI) planned for the boost-phase defense on Phase I. There were several reasons that apparently motivated this change:

1. The original SBI proposed for the boost-phase defense did not use "exotic technology," so the first space-based tests planned for SBI on Phase I would apparently violate even the broad interpretation of the ABM Treaty.

2. The ending of the cold war changed the emphasis on the role of strategic defense.

3. The cost of Phase I deployment appeared to decrease with this change.

4. The novelty of the Brilliant Pebbles concept was more likely to gain political support for strategic defense.

Brilliant Pebbles is a technology upgrade of the older Smart Rocks system. In the early sixties, the Air Force examined an idea for such an antiballistic missile system called BAMBI (Ballistic Missile Boost-phase Intercept). However, the huge size required for adequate computers and sensors made it clear that this system was not workable.

The High Frontier concept proposed by Gen. Daniel Graham in the late 1970s was a refinement of the Smart Rocks idea. This involved putting a large number of "trucks" in orbit over the Soviet ICBM fields, each truck containing a number of homing rockets. High Frontier received widespread criticism in the next few years because it had many of the severe flaws of BAMBI. Two of these flaws were:

1. Interception would take place 350 seconds after the missile launch was detected, whereas the Soviet SS-18s had a boost phase of only 300 seconds. Interception could not take place until about two minutes (adding the time for detection and tracking) *after* the end of the boost phase, when most of the warheads would already have been deployed.

2. The 432 orbiting trucks (each with 45 kinetic kill vehicles) proposed could only cover 12% of the ICBMs.

Such a defense would be useless even with no Soviet countermeasures.[1]

The Brilliant Pebbles concept was a technological upgrade of the old Smart Rocks idea in which the recent advances in computer technology would be used to develop smaller and more capable weapons that avoided the flaws of the old BAMBI proposal (some people have dubbed them "smart Smart Rocks"). Each Brilliant Pebble is autonomous with its own sensors, computational intelligence, power, capability for propulsion, and area to defend (see the diagram in Figure E.1). Their independence avoids the problem of crippling the defense by taking out vulnerable critical systems. However, the defense has a critical connection to U.S. military command centers necessary for activation.[2]

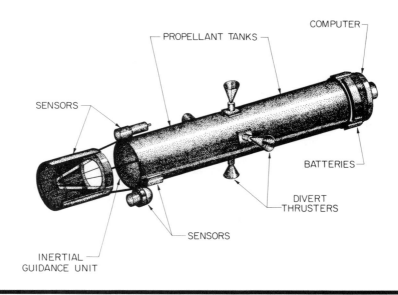

Fig. E.1. Conceptual form of a Brilliant Pebble interceptor, which is about 1 meter in length.

Although certain aspects of the Brilliant Pebbles appear to make them more promising candidates for defense, there are clear limits on this capability. Two important questions are addressed with calculations in Appendix 23: (1) how many Brilliant Pebbles are required for an effective boost-phase defense against a large-scale attack, and (2) what are the capabilities of the 4,000 planned for a Phase I defense?

The analysis of the requirements for a boost-phase defense against 1,000 warheads on clustered single-warhead missiles similar to the Soviet SS-25s shows that at least 80,000 will be required, assuming no effective countermeasures against the Brilliant Pebbles are employed and a minimum 30-second response time is achieved. This minimum requirement scales up rapidly as the available boost-phase time decreases. For example, if the boost-phase time of the ICBMs is scaled down to 150 seconds (the fastest time on current U.S. missiles) and the response time is more realistically 60 seconds, the required number of Brilliant Pebbles increases to 175,000. (Lieutenant General George Monahan testified before the Senate Appropriations Committee in early 1990 that the detection and preparation time would be from 50 to 100 seconds.) Furthermore, minimum requirements for use of this defense against current SLBMs are two to three times as great.

The direct cost of each Brilliant Pebble has been estimated to be around $1 million (higher than the earlier estimates of $500,000 mentioned in Chapter 7). The direct cost of the 80,000–175,000 minimum needed for defense against 1,000 single-warhead ICBMs is around $100 billion–$150 billion. When the indirect costs of development, deployment, and maintenance of the defense after deployment are added, this minimal boost-phase part of the defense against 1,000 warheads could easily be $500 billion. On the other hand, the direct cost of 1,000 Soviet single-warhead SS-25s is $20 billion–$30 billion, so the minimum (defense/offense) cost ratio is around 5. Thus Brilliant Pebbles is not cost effective against SS-25s.

ICBMs deployed with fast-burn boosters cannot be intercepted until after the end of the boost phase and likely after most of the warheads have already been deployed. Adding a fast-burn booster to SS-25s increases the cost of each SS-25 to $60 million but makes the booster invulnerable to Brilliant Pebbles (sending the cost ratio to infinity). The interceptors become almost totally ineffective as a defense. Thus Brilliant Pebbles can at most serve as an interim defense until these boosters are deployed.

The SDIO plans to deploy 4,000 Brilliant Pebbles with the Phase I defense. This plan clearly indicates that the defense is not intended to defend against a large-scale attack, but rather against an attack consisting of only a few boosters. Brilliant Pebbles was originally set forth as a limited defense to protect against the imaginary first-strike capability of the Soviets. That intention appears to have been modifed with the ending of the cold war to more recently discussed goals of protecting against an accidental nuclear strike and Third World nuclear arms development.

However, can Brilliant Pebbles be deployed in this more restrictive capacity that does not encourage an offensive buildup, as planned for a Phase I defense? While that would certainly be possible if the defense was cost effective (that is, it would cost less than the offensive buildup necessary to overcome it), the fact that it is not cost effective against the new SS-25s leaves serious doubts about this prospect. These doubts are substantially increased when one considers the close connection of the defense technologies with ASATs, the fact that Brilliant Pebble devices have potential capability for ASAT use, and the fact that the United States is actively pursuing ASAT development. (The ASAT problem is addressed in greater depth in the next section.)

Can a Brilliant Pebbles defense be useful in avoiding an accidental nuclear launch? To achieve this goal the coverage cannot be limited to ICBM coverage of the Soviet missile fields but must be worldwide coverage of Soviet SLBMs and possible nuclear missiles of other countries. The calculations of Appendix 23 seem to imply that a defense concentrated over the Soviet ICBM fields will be able to protect the launch of a small number of ICBMs (without fast-burn boosters) launched accidentally. However, a revised system for worldwide coverage will give a significantly lower protection against an accidental SLBM launch. Furthermore it will give us no protection against an accidental cruise missile launch.

With the $55 billion direct-cost estimate (a very conservative estimate) for this Phase I defense and the indirect costs for development, deployment, and maintenance, the total costs will be several hundred billion dollars. The $55 billion estimate has been questioned by the General Accounting Office because there have been no architecture studies on the structure of a defense with Brilliant Pebbles (the architecture studies for a Phase I defense were based on using the original Space-Based Interceptors for a boost-phase component).[3] Pursuing this very expensive and very limited approach to prevention is undoubtedly less wise than exploring other less expensive and more reliable ways of preventing accidental nuclear war.

Using a strategic defense to protect against Third World missiles carrying chemical or nuclear weapons is similar to using an elephant gun to protect against distant "killer" bees. Iraq is one of the few countries with missiles, and these missiles are short range (they can reach Israel) and fly too low for a strategic defense to counter. Furthermore, although Third World missiles could never come anywhere close to the United

States, chemical or nuclear weapons could be delivered to the United States on ships or aircrafts. A strategic defense provides no protection against available means of Third World weapon delivery or against terrorism. Possible Third World threats provide no justification for developing an expensive missile defense.

As a final note, the technology for Brilliant Pebbles is still in its infancy. In 1988 it first came to light in SDI as an advanced technology concept, and its attractiveness as a replacement for the original flawed SBI boost-phase defense led to its quick adoption for a Phase I defense. However, unseen problems may come to light in its development, and the eventual direct cost of the interceptors may easily be substantially more than $1 million. It can be compared with the Advanced Medium-Range Air-to-Air Missile (AMRAAM), anti-aircraft weapon that has some similarities to (but a much simpler mission than) the planned Brilliant Pebbles. That weapon now costs five times its original estimated cost and has encountered several performance and reliability problems in its development. Whether Brilliant Pebbles will suffer a similar fate remains to be seen.

New Antisatellite Weapons and Accidental Nuclear War

The strategic defense program has suffered a setback with the sizeable budget reduction for FY 1991. However, that may not hinder the development of several of the technologies associated with SDI because of the ASAT applications. As discussed in Chapter 8, technologies developed for countering missiles are much more effective in countering orbiting satellites and can be developed for that capability much faster than they can be developed for countering missiles. Furthermore, ASATs can be developed at less expense, and the budgetary constraints on developing these technologies for SDI use do not apply to the development of ASATs.

As mentioned in Chapter 8, since 1977 the Air Force had been developing an ASAT called the Miniature Homing Vehicle (MHV), which would be launched from an F-15. This program was ended in 1988 as a result of congressional restrictions on the ASAT testing, which were imposed in response to the Soviet moratorium on ASAT testing. The developments in homing rockets as a result of MHV and related defense programs provided a motivation for the SDI shift to phase deployment in early 1987.

The Pentagon is actively pursuing the use of other technologies developed under SDI for ASATs. One example is the $2.2 million chemical laser (MIRACL, for Mid-Infrared Advanced Chemical Laser) at the White Sands missile range, which had begun for SDI experiments. Frank Carlucci, secretary of defense from 1987 to 1989, directed that it be converted into use for directed-energy ASAT testing in late 1988. Testing of the facility is scheduled for 1991.

In January 1989 Carlucci spoke of a need for U.S. ASATs, claiming that "the development and deployment of a comprehensive ASAT capability is an absolute necessity," with the United States' lack of operational ASATs the "single and most vulnerable point" of our defense. Carlucci proposed new development of ASATs with programs in all three branches of the armed services.

The Department of Defense is also targeting the free-electron laser, which receives over $100 million a year from SDI-funded development, for possible anti-satellite use. In FY 1990 $15 million was allocated for free-electron laser ASAT development, and a sizeable increase to $41 million was requested for FY 1991. The Army's free-electron laser is a potential candidate for eventual directed-energy ASAT use.

A spinoff of the Army's SDI program to develop midcourse kinetic-energy weapons is a new program for use of SDI kinetic-energy weapon technology to shoot heat-seeking interceptors to counter low-orbiting spacecraft. The Army program was initiated with the Defense Acquisition Board's approval in March 1989. In FY 1989 $74 million was allocated for the program, with $208 million requested for FY 1990. Contracts are being negotiated for developing and testing seekers, sensors, kill mechanisms, and other SDI components. Flight tests may begin as early as 1992. A system of 60–75 rockets is planned for deployment in the mid-1990s.

The Army ASAT is based on technology from the Exoatmospheric Reentry Interceptor System (ERIS) that is being developed for midcourse defense in a Phase I strategic defense (discussed in Chapter 7). This has been noted by strategic defense managers as well as Army representatives. By using three-stage boosters on the rocket, this ASAT could eventually be able to counter satellites in geosynchronous orbit (23,000 miles or 36,000 kilometers out). Currently the United States has 26 military communication satellites, 5 early-warning satellites, and 4 intelligence satellites in geosynchronous orbit. The Soviet Union only has 2 communication satellites in geosynchronous orbit, but many more than the United States (69 to 24) in the vulnerable low Earth orbits.[4]

If Brilliant Pebbles interceptors are deployed for a Phase I defense, they will also have ready use as ASATs, and if they are deployed in a worldwide coverage for the purpose of preventing accidental nuclear launch, ASAT capability will be extended. If the interceptors are capable of destroying missiles, they will be much more capable of destroying satellites. Furthermore, they will have the significant advantage of surprise when used to attack satellites. The Brilliant Pebbles will provide deadly ASAT capability, and the possibility of that use will cause concern to the Soviets and possibly other countries with satellites.

Although it is claimed that one purpose of having a limited antimissile defense is avoiding an accidental nuclear war, the ASAT technology and capability arising from strategic defense development and deployment significantly increases the danger of an accidental nuclear war! As discussed in Chapter 8 satellites provide essential information on nuclear developments through reconnaissance, treaty verification, and early warning. They also provide essential links in naval military communications. If crucial information or communication is denied through ASAT destruction of satellites, especially in a time of crisis when such attacks are more likely, the reduced critical information could lead to an accidental nuclear launch.

It is much more important to ban ASATs to ensure the resulting stability to help prevent an accidental nuclear launch than it is to deploy an anti-missile defense that may or may not be effective in countering an accidental launch. If a Phase I defense is deployed with Brilliant Pebbles over the Soviet ICBM fields, it may encourage the Soviets to develop ASATs that are capable of countering them. This will stimulate U.S. ASAT development and deployment. Thus deployment of a strategic defense is just as likely to increase the chances of an accidental nuclear war.

The chance of an accidental nuclear war is a significant concern that requires several steps to reduce. In addition to banning ASATs, several other changes to avoid an accidental nuclear war were recommended by U.S. and Soviet weapons experts at a 1989 meeting in Washington, D.C.[5]

1. *Halt the counterforce weapon competition and eliminate the most destabilizing counterforce weapons (ones with several MIRVed vehicles).* (The dangers of the buildup of counterforce missile deployment and the possible perceived first-strike threat of MIRVed counterforce weapons, especially when combined with an anti-missile defense, were discussed in Chapter 8.)

2. *Reject launch-on-warning.* While neither side has adopted this policy, the presence of only adequate retaliatory forces will help ensure that both sides can adopt a convincing wait-and-see posture.

3. *Establish in-country warning systems in addition to early-warning systems.* Early-warning systems generate several false alarms, and the time pressure in a false alarm could lead to an accidental nuclear launch. However, on-site verification allows each side to put sensors at missile sites in

the other country, which could be transmitted by a relay satellite, providing a verification of a launch.

4. *Strengthen central controls.* Rejecting launch-on-warning allows for a tighter control of all nuclear weapon systems. One suggestion is to place permissive action links on all missiles.

5. *Install command-destruct systems on all missiles.* These could be similar to the command-destruct system that allows a safety officer to destroy a test missile in the event of a test failure. Currently, once a missile is launched, there is no means to stop it if an error is discovered shortly after launch. Having command-destruct systems that are activated by a secret code provides a more reliable way to end the launch than hoping that anti-missile defense systems can do the job.

Making these changes and innovations is a more useful agenda for avoiding accidental nuclear war than spending a large bankroll to develop and deploy a strategic defense that is unreliable in this prevention.

Table E.1. Chronology of major events related to SDI and space weapons

Date	Event
3/83	President Ronald Reagan's speech initiated SDI (see Appendix 1).
10/83	The Hoffman Commission released a classified study on the role of strategic defense systems in future U.S. security strategy.
1/84	The Department of Defense (DOD) created SDI as a research and technology program and initiated the creation of SDIO.
1/84	The first ASAT test of a homing rocket launched from an F-15 aircraft was conducted by the Air Force.
2/84	President Reagan asked for $2 billion for the first annual budget of the SDI program. Congress eventually reduced the budget to $1.4 billion.
3/84	The Fletcher Defense Studies Technology Team released its report, recommending a crash program to develop defense capability.
4/84	SDIO, the fourth branch of the armed services, was formally chartered.
6/84	The Homing Overlay Experiment was carried out, in which a homing rocket destroyed a dummy ICBM warhead.
12/84	President Reagan met with Prime Minister Margaret Thatcher to discuss British concerns over SDI.
2/85	President Reagan sought an expansion of the second annual SDI budget to $3.7 billion. Congress eventually reduced it to $2.75 billion.
3/85	Secretary of Defense Casper Weinberger addressed the Nuclear Planning Group in Luxembourg, inviting NATO and other allied nations to participate in facets of U.S. SDI research.
4/85	Geneva arms talks between the United States and the Soviet Union were stalemated with major disagreements over linking space weapons with strategic and intermediate-range missiles.
10/85	National Security Advisor Robert McFarlane publicly announced the "broad interpretation" of the ABM Treaty, which permits testing and development of new "exotic technologies."

Table E.1. Chronology of major events related to SDI and space weapons (*continued*)

Date	Event
10/85	SDIO released its first architecture (system design) studies. The one favored had 7 layers of defense and thousands of defense satellites divided among the boost, post-boost, midcourse, and terminal phases. Other architectures were for a purely terminal defense.
12/85	The first Reagan-Gorbachev summit was held at Geneva. No compromises were reached on space weapons, and the only agreement reached was to step up arms negotiations.
12/85	The report by the SDI Panel on Computing in Support of Battle Management (the Eastport Study Group) concluded that the hardware and software needed for SDI are possible but extremely complex.
12/85	Great Britain agreed to cooperate on facets of SDI research. West Germany soon followed suit.
1/86	France rejected cooperation on facets of SDI research. Norway, Denmark, Belgium, the Netherlands, and Sweden soon followed suit.
2/86	President Reagan sought $4.8 billion for the third annual SDI budget. Congress eventually reduced it to $3.2 billion.
9/86	The first Delta test, in which a homing rocket tracked and intercepted a Delta missile, was performed.
10/86	The second Reagan-Gorbachev summit was held in Reykjavik, Iceland. SDI was a major stumbling block, as President Reagan refused to accept limitations on SDI in exchange for deep reductions in Soviet armed forces.
1/87	President Reagan sought $5.8 billion for the fourth annual SDI budget. Congress eventually reduced it to $3.6 billion.
1/87	Early deployment of a first-phase defense using homing rocket interceptors was endorsed by Secretary of Defense Weinburger.
3/87	Senator Sam Nunn, chair of the Senate Armed Services Committee, publicly challenged the broad interpretation of the ABM Treaty.
5/87	Geneva arms control negotiations were held between the United States and the Soviet Union on reductions of long-range and intermediate-range missiles.
7/87	SDIO proposed a Phase I architecture to the Defense Acquisition Board.
9/87	Secretary of Defense Weinberger directed concept demonstration and validation for Phase I of the defense (the beginning of the test phase for SDI).
12/87	A Reagan-Gorbachev summit was held in Washington, D.C., to sign the INF Treaty, which was ratified by the Senate the following May.
1/88	The ALPS proposal was presented to the Senate Armed Services Committee by its chairman, Senator Sam Nunn.
2/88	President Reagan sought $4.6 billion for the fifth annual SDI budget. Congress eventually approved $3.7 billion.
2/88	The Delta test for the ability of sensors to detect and track simulated targets was carried out.
5/88	A Reagan-Gorbachev summit was held in Moscow. They exchanged documents on each country's ratification of the INF Treaty, but no new agreements were reached.
6/88	A GAO report concluded that Edward Teller's assertions to President Reagan before SDI began that the X-ray laser were ready for the engineering phase were technical optimism, but not deception.
Summer/88	Brilliant Pebbles, proposed by Lowell Wood, became an advanced technology concept in SDI.

Table E.1. Chronology of major events related to SDI and space weapons (*continued*)

Date	Event
10/88	The $115 billion estimate by SDIO for the direct cost of a Phase I defense was decreased to $69 billion by cutting the planned Space-Based Interceptor forces in half.
Fall/88	SDIO adopted an architecture for a Phase I defense using SBI, ERIS, and HEDI homing rocket interceptors.
1/89	Lt. Gen. James Abrahamson ended his position as the director of SDIO. Lt. Gen. George Monahan succeeded as the new director.
2/89	President Bush addressed Congress saying that he would vigorously pursue the strategic defense program.
3/89	The Delta Star test was conducted to test the ability of sensors to detect plumes from rockets launched.
5/89	The Bush administration initiated a study on the possible substitution of Brilliant Pebbles for the Space-Based Interceptors in a Phase I defense.
6/89	The BEAR test was conducted for the firing of a neutral beam, oriented toward the possible development of a neutral beam in midcourse discrimination.
1/90	SDIO incorporated Brilliant Pebbles into the Phase I defense system design as a replacement for the Space-Based Interceptor as the boost-phase defense component.
2/90	President Bush proposed $4.6 billion for the fiscal 1991 SDI budget. Congress eventually reduced it to $2.9 billion.
2/90	The RME/LACE test satellites were launched to study mirror relaying of laser beams and correction of atmospheric distortions, oriented toward developing a mirror anti-missile system (discussed in Chap. 3) for a future Phase II defense.
5/90	The long-delayed flight test on a Boeing 767 of AOA, which is being developed for terminal-phase detection and tracking, was carried out. This is considered a likely violation of the 1972 ABM Treaty (the permissive interpretation discussed in Chap. 10) because it appears capable of working as a mobile anti-missile radar.
6/90	A summit in Washington, D.C., was held between Bush and Gorbachev, but strategic defense was not discussed. The next summit was scheduled for 2/91 in Moscow.
7/90	Henry Cooper became the new director of SDIO (the first civilian director), replacing retiring Lt. Gen. Monahan.
7/90	Hovering test for SBI carried out, in which a prototype kinetic interceptor hovered in position while its microwave radio sensor locked onto a passing satellite.

Planned Future Decisions

1993	Presidential decision on deploying Phase I. The President must submit to Congress a certification that the defense system can satisfy the cost effectiveness and stability criteria set by Public Law 99-145 (Appendix 14).
1995	Acquisition decision by DOD on full-scale "development" (building, testing, and readying for production) of Phase I defense.

Note: A very good chronology of political events and proclamations on ABM and SDI ranging from 1959 to early 1987 is contained in Douglas C. Waller, James T. Bruce, and Douglas M. Cook, *The Strategic Defense Initiative: Progress and Challenges* (Claremont, Calif.: Regina Books, 1987). An excellent detailed history on the politics and developments in SDI is given by Sanford Lakoff and Herbert F. York, *A Shield in Space? Technology, Politics, and the Strategic Defense Initiative* (University of California Press, 1989).

Latter Part of President Reagan's National Address on March 23, 1983

The first part of President Reagan's address dealt with issues regarding the national defense. He started the address with "The subject I want to discuss with you, peace and national security, is both timely and important—timely because I have reached a decision which offers a new hope for our children in the 21st century—a decision I will tell you about in a few minutes—and important because there is a very big decision that you must make yourselves." The new decision was the start of the Strategic Defense Initiative. The big decision the citizens of the nations must make had to do with the question of support for Reagan's military program and budget. After discussing a number of national defense policy issues and the situation of Soviet nuclear arms buildup, he then detailed the decision he had made. The following text is the latter part of his speech.

Now, thus far tonight I have shared with you my thoughts on the problems of national security we must face together. My predecessors in the Oval Office have appeared before you on other occasions to describe the threat posed by Soviet power and have proposed steps to address that threat. But since the advent of nuclear weapons, those steps have been increasingly directed toward deterrence of aggression through the promise of retaliation.

This approach to stability through offensive threat has worked. We and our allies have succeeded in three decades. In recent months, however,

Source: *New York Times,* March 24, 1983.

my advisors, including in particular the joint chiefs of staff, have under-scored the necessity to break out of a future that relies solely on offensive retaliation for our security.

Over the course of these discussions, I have become more and more deeply convinced that the human spirit must be capable of rising above dealing with other nations and human beings by threatening their exist-ence. Feeling this way, I believe we must thoroughly examine every oppor-tunity for reducing tensions and for introducing greater stability into the strategic calculus on both sides.

One of the most important contributions we can make is, of course, to lower the level of all arms, and particularly nuclear arms. We are engaged right now in several negotiations with the Soviet Union to bring about a mutual reduction of weapons. I will report to you a week from tomorrow my thoughts on that score. But let me just say I am totally committed to this course.

If the Soviet Union will join with us in our effort to achieve major arms reduction we will have succeeded in stabilizing the nuclear balance. Nevertheless it will still be necessary to rely on the specter of retaliation — on mutual threat, and that is a sad commentary on the human condition. Wouldn't it be better to save lives than to condemn them? Are we not capable of demonstrating our peaceful intentions by applying all our abili-ties and our ingenuity to achieving a truly lasting stability? I think we are. Indeed, we must!

After careful consultation with my advisers, including the Joint Chiefs of Staff, I believe there is a way. Let me share with you a vision of the future which offers hope. It is that we embark on a program to counter the awesome Soviet missile threat with measures that are defensive. Let us turn to the very strengths in technology that spawned our great industrial base and that have given us the quality of life we enjoy today.

What if free people could live secure in the knowledge that their security did not rest upon the threat of US retaliation to deter a Soviet attack; that we could intercept and destroy strategic ballistic missiles be-fore they reached our own soil or that of our allies?

I know this is a formidable technical task, one that may not be accom plished before the end of this century. Yet, current technology has attained a level of sophistication where it is reasonable for us to begin this effort. It will take years, probably decades, of effort on many fronts. There will be failures and setbacks just as there will be successes and breakthroughs. And as we proceed we must remain constant in preserving the nuclear deterrent and maintaining a solid capability for flexible response. But isn't it worth every investment necessary to free the world from the threat of nuclear war? We know it is!

In the meantime, we will continue to pursue real reductions in nuclear arms, negotiating from a position of strength that can be ensured only by modernizing our strategic forces. At the same time, we must take steps to reduce the risk of a conventional military conflict escalating into a nuclear war by improving our non-nuclear capabilities.

America does possess — now — the technologies to attain very significant improvements in the effectiveness of our conventional non-nuclear forces. Proceeding boldly with these new technologies, we can significantly reduce any incentive that the Soviet Union may have to threaten attack against the United States or it allies.

As we pursue our goal of defensive technologies, we recognize that our allies rely upon our strategic offensive power to deter attacks against them. Their vital interests and ours are inextricably linked — their safety and ours are one. And no change in technology can or will alter that reality. We must and shall continue to honor our commitments.

I clearly recognize that defensive systems have limitations and raise certain problems and ambiguities. If paired with offensive systems, they can be viewed as fostering an aggressive policy and no one wants that.

But with these considerations firmly in mind, I call upon the scientific community in our country, those who gave us nuclear weapons, to turn their great talents now to the cause of mankind and world peace: to give us the means of rendering these nuclear weapons impotent and obsolete.

Tonight, consistent with our obligations under the ABM Treaty and recognizing the need for closer consultation with our allies, I am taking an important first step. I am directing a comprehensive and intensive effort to define a long-term research and development program to begin to achieve our ultimate goal of eliminating the threat posed by strategic nuclear missiles. This could pave the way for arms control measures to eliminate the weapons themselves. We seek neither military superiority nor political advantage. Our only purpose — one all people share — is to search for ways to reduce the danger of nuclear war.

My fellow Americans, tonight we are launching an effort which holds the promise of changing the course of human history. There will be risks, and results take time. But I believe we can do it. As we cross this threshold, I ask for your prayers and your support. Thank you, good night and God bless you.

APPENDIX 2

Basic Principles of a Laser

The principles governing the operation of a laser can be explained with the aid of Figure A2.1. The laser consists of a lasing medium in a tuned cavity. (These are the first two components of a laser.) The lasing medium can be a solid, liquid, gas, or plasma, although solid lasers are generally of too low a power to be of interest for defensive weapons. The molecules of the lasing medium have internal electron energy levels. According to quantum mechanics, the electrons occupy discrete energy levels in the molecule in general. For simplicity, assume the molecule only has two energy levels: an upper one and a lower one.

The electrons can move from a lower energy level to an upper energy level by absorbing a photon (of light, X-rays, etc.), and can move from the upper energy level to a lower level by emitting a photon. The frequency f of the photon is given by $hf = E_1 - E_2$, where h is Planck's constant, equal to 6.6×10^{-34} joule-sec, and E_1 and E_2 are the energies of the two levels in electron volts [see Figure A2.1(a)]. The laser cavity is tuned to the frequency of the photons of interest (forming a so-called cavity resonator, the first component necessary for a laser).

A second component of the laser is a pump, or energy source. This pump is used to excite the electrons into their upper state, and can take a variety of forms, such as electrical discharges, chemical reactions, etc. Electrons that are in the upper state can decay to the lower state in one of two ways. There are a small number of upper-state electrons that decay initially to the lower state spontaneously, giving rise to spontaneous emission of photons of the radiation. These spontaneously emitted photons can stimulate a larger number of upper-state electrons to decay, giving rise to stimulated emission of radiation. However, the emitted photons also stimulate electrons that are in the lower state to absorb them and jump to the upper state, giving stimulated absorption of radiation. If a "population inversion" exists initially—i.e., if there are more electrons in the upper level than the lower level after the electrons are pumped—there is a net gain of free photons occurring in these processes. The population inversion in the lasing medium is required for lasing to occur and is the third component of the laser.

The fourth and final component of the laser is a feedback mechanism to enhance the stimulated emission and provide for a buildup of a substantial amount of power in the emitted radiation. This is supplied by the presence of a reflecting mirror on one side of the laser and a partially

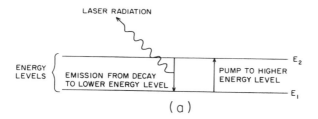

(a)

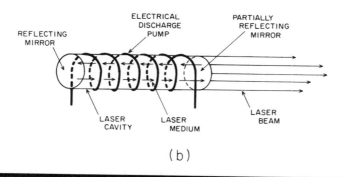

(b)

Fig. A2.1. (a) Emission and absorption of photons by electrons making transitions to lower or higher energy levels. If there are more electrons in the higher energy level emitting than in the lower energy level absorbing them, a population inversion exists and lasing can occur. (b) The other three basic components of a laser: the pump, the resonant cavity, the mirrors for feedback.

reflecting mirror on the other side [see an illustration of the four components for a very simple laser in Figure A2.1(b)]. When these four components are combined, the result is a beam of light or some other kind of radiation that is monochromatic and phase coherent. The laser beam has enhanced power and limited diffraction. It comes out in the form of a pencil beam, in contrast to the beam of a flashlight, which comes out in a broader cone because the source is phase incoherent.

Mechanisms of Laser Target Damage

When a normal powerful laser beam impacts on an object, there are two types of damage that occur. The first is thermal damage from the heat generated, which can weaken the metal and melt or even vaporize the surface. The second is mechanical damage. This can result from the sudden large current that is generated in the metal by the impulse. It also comes from the thermal shock wave created by the sudden heating that takes place. An analysis of the power required to achieve these destruction processes shows that over a megajoule of energy per square centimeter is needed.

However, the laser beam can be designed to cause greater damage than results from these processes. This is because the beam can be tailored to cause thermomechanical damage, a kind of synergism between the thermal and mechanical damage. There are two ways this can be done. The first is attained by using a repetitively pulsed source, so successive bursts do the damage, rather than just a continuous wave form. The thermomechanical effects produce a plastic strain in the metal which accumulates after each burst until destruction has occurred. The other way is to alternate between a continuous wave operation for a short time followed by a radiation pulse. The continuous wave operation causes the heating and weakens the metal because of the thermal effects, and the pulse generates the mechanical force that can punch a hole through the weakened metal. Both are necessary to burn through the metal.

The net result of the synergistic use of these two damage mechanisms is to lower substantially the energy fluence required to a minimum of about 10–20 kilojoules per square centimeter. In the calculations made in the other appendices, the lower figure for the kill energy fluence (denoted by J) is used.

APPENDIX 4

How the Chemical Laser Works

The most promising type of chemical laser that is being developed for use in the boost phase of a (latter-phase) ballistic-missile defense system is the hydrogen fluoride (HF) laser or its companion, the deuterium (a heavy isotope of hydrogen) fluoride (DF) laser. These lasers are the most powerful of the molecular gas lasers. The HF laser operates at a wavelength of 2.7 microns and the DF laser at about 4 microns, both in the infrared.

The pumping energy for the laser is supplied by chemical reaction: $H_2 + F_2 \to 2HF$, where H_2 and F_2 are hydrogen and fluorine in their normal diatomic form. A continuous reaction is sustained by the presence of monatomic H and F with the diatomic molecules, creating the reaction cycle with a two-step process: (1) $H + F_2 \to HF + F$ and (2) $F + H_2 \to HF + H$. (See Figure A4.1.)

Part of the energy that is produced by this chemical reaction is absorbed by electrons of the molecule as they are stimulated into a higher-energy orbital. The larger number of hydrogen fluoride molecules with their outer electrons in the upper-energy state, compared to the number with outer electrons in the lower-energy unexcited state, as a result of the chemical reaction creates a population inversion that is necessary for the lasing to take place. The reaction cycle is kept ongoing by continually pumping new hydrogen and fluorine into the reaction chamber and pumping out hydrogen fluoride, causing the laser to continually operate.

The infrared beam created by the HF laser is strongly absorbed by the Earth's atmosphere, so the lasers can only be used for exoatmospheric (space-based) defense applications. The DF laser is more effective in penetrating the atmosphere, so it could access objects much lower in the at-

160

mosphere. The chemical laser would be based on a defense station in low Earth orbit a few hundred miles above the Earth's surface.

Other molecular reactions are being explored for other varieties of powerful chemical lasers, but these are not as well developed as the hydrogen fluoride laser. A technical survey of the hydrogen fluoride laser, iodine lasers, and other chemical lasers undergoing research is contained in the report of the American Physical Society study group.[1]

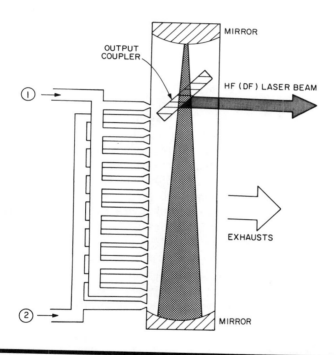

Fig. A4.1. Basic configuration of a chemical (hydrogen fluoride) laser. Input 1 consists of F_2 (or another fluorine compound such as NF_3) along with some H_2 or D_2 to produce HF or DF. Input 2 consists of a larger quantity of H_2 or D_2 to provide a sustained chemical reaction for pumping inside the laser chamber. [Adapted from "The Science and Technology of Directed-Energy Weapons," in *Reviews of Modern Physics* 59 (July 1987): S1-S200]

APPENDIX 5

Number of Satellites Needed for a Chemical-Laser Defense

In the chemical-laser satellite system for the missile boost-phase defense a critical question on the costs involved is how many satellites would be necessary. One may put a minimum on the number required by determining how many would be necessary to cover the Soviet missile fields to take out most of the missiles launched by the Soviets (there are 1,400 ICBMs at present, but there will very likely be more by the time of deployment of a chemical laser missile defense). A 90% boost-phase kill is necessary to break even (to have only as many targets to destroy after boost phase as one did in the boost phase), and several satellites would be needed in orbit for every one that would be over the Soviet missile fields.

This question was addressed in a detailed calculation by Richard Garwin.[1] (A discussion of these calculations is also in Bethe and Garwin.)[2] The number of satellites required depends upon the number of Soviet missiles (M), the minimum energy fluence required to destroy a missile (J), the available boost-phase time (T_o), the time (T_s) for slewing and settling the laser beam after each targeting. For missile silos spread uniformly between 50° and 60° latitude, the optimal orbital configuration for coverage is for orbits inclined about 60° with respect to the equator. These orbits were assumed in the analysis, which minimizes the number of defense satellites needed to cover the Soviet ICBM fields, concentrating the defense satellites by a factor of 3.1 from a uniform global coverage. Garwin assumed laser powers of $P = 25$ megawatts, wavelengths $\lambda = 2.7 \times 10^{-6}$ meters (the operating wavelength of a hydrogen-fluoride laser), and a diffraction-limited mirror diameter of 10 meters, which gives a laser brightness $B = \pi PD^2/4\lambda^2 = 2.69 \times 10^{20}$ watts/steradian. The energy fluence required to kill a missile was taken as $J = 20$ kilojoules per square centimeter.

Assuming one missile is destroyed for every laser firing (100% accuracy), the results on the minimum requirements for defense satellites are summarized in Table A5.1 for two models of missile distribution. The term S_1 is the minimum number of satellites required for a model in which the ICBMs are uniformly distributed over a large area in the Soviet Union lying between 50° and 60° latitude — 10 million square kilometers or about 4 million square miles. The calculation for this model used the flat-Earth approximation, whereas the roundness of the Earth will slightly increase the numbers. The term S_2 is the minimum number of satellites for a round-Earth model in which the ICBMs are concentrated in a small area.

Table A5.1. Number of chemical-laser satellites needed

M	T_o (sec)	T_s (sec)	S_1	S_2
1,400	100	3.0	697	381
3,000	100	3.0	1,485	817
1,400	100	0.5	146	251
3,000	100	0.5	281	537
1,400	100	0.1	79	187
3,000	100	0.1	126	401
1,400	40	3.0	1,732	953
3,000	40	3.0	3,699	2,044
1,400	40	0.5	322	628
3,000	40	0.5	653	1,344
1,400	40	0.1	138	468
3,000	40	0.1	228	1,003

Note: M = number of Soviet missiles launched; T_o = boost-phase time (seconds) available for countering missiles; T_s = slew and settle time (seconds) after each laser firing; S = number of defense satellites required for models 1 and 2.

The first (uniform missile distribution) model is a crude approximation for the current distribution of Soviet missile fields, which was used in some earlier calculations of the number of satellites necessary for this defense. The second model is a more realistic one for future Soviet missile basing as a counter to development and deployment of a chemical laser defense, since the clustered basing in general will increase the minumum number of satellites required to cover the missiles (with the exception of slew and settle times of longer than a second). A typical case from Table A5.1 is for optimum coverage of 3,000 ICBMs in a clustered basing with 100 seconds of the boost-phase time available for targeting, and 0.5 second slew and settle time. For these conditions, 537 satellites will be needed to cover the Soviet missiles.

The minimum number of satellites needed will increase when potential errors in the targeting are considered, since the model assumes one missile destroyed for every laser firing. If the accuracy of the targeting is only 50%, then a minimum of 1,074 satellites will be required for the same conditions, while if the accuracy is only 25%, then 2,148 will be needed. The accuracy in the targeting cannot be predicted accurately ahead of time, particularly since the Soviets have several options in the way they may proceed with an attack.

The effectiveness of destroying the targets may depend on other factors in addition to the accuracy of the laser beams. The number of defense satellites needed may also be influenced by the probability of defense stations working properly at the critical time when they are needed, or by the probability that the defense satellite survives the complete boost phase from an attack by Soviet missiles. It was assumed in this calculation that both of these probabilities are 100%, but they assuredly will not be that value in an actual use against a Soviet strike. There is always a finite probability that a critical part will fail some of the systems. Furthermore, the Soviets will be developing means for attacking the defense while we are starting to deploy it, so part of the defense will be destroyed by such an attack.

An important factor of this defense is the cost for the deployment of new missiles compared to the cost of the extra defense to counter the extra missiles. A study was made by George Field and Dave Spergel on the ratio of these differential costs (defense incremental cost over offense incremental cost) assuming 100% accuracy.[3] For the case of 1,400 missiles with 25 megawatt lasers, 10-meter diameter mirrors and a required energy fluence of 20 kJ/cm² (the same parameters as in the Garwin calculation), the cost-exchange ratio (CER) is shown in Table A5.2 for values of the boost-phase time available for targeting (T_o) and the retarget time for the lasers (T_s). For example, for a 100-second boost-phase time and a 0.5 second retarget

Table A5.2. Cost-exchange ratios: Incremental defense costs over incremental offense costs

T_o (sec)	T_s (sec)	CER
100	3.0	13
100	0.5	7.5
100	0.1	5.2
50	3.0	22
50	0.5	13
50	0.1	8.8
40	3.0	26
40	0.5	15
40	0.1	11

time, the incremental cost for the defense is 7.5 times as expensive as the incremental cost of the offense.

For the conditions in Table A5.2, the cost-exchange ratio ranges from 5 to 26. Clearly the added cost of the orbiting-laser defense will considerably exceed that added cost for the offense it is designed to counter. This will encourage the Soviets to build up their offensive forces as a countermeasure, as discussed in Chapter 6.

How the X-ray Laser Works and the Laser Gain Achievable

The idea for a nuclear-explosion-pumped X-ray laser was developed by a group headed by Dr. Edward Teller at Lawrence Livermore Laboratory around 1980, with MIT student Peter Hagelstein introducing the key physics. Most of the research associated with the X-ray-laser defensive weapon is classified.

To achieve the intensities of radiation desired at these short wavelengths requires a very large power source. The prodigious amount needed can be attained in a nuclear explosion, which serves as the pump. The explosion destroys the weapon, so the power must be generated in the extremely short time between the ignition of the explosion and disintegration of the laser structure (a few billionths of a second).

At X-ray wavelengths there are no mirrors or coherent reflectors available, so the laser does not utilize feedback or true cavity resonators. Thus the X-ray beam emerges in a small cone whose angular spread is determined by the wavelength and geometric size of the source.

The laser is composed of a number of rods consisting of fibers surrounded by diffuse lead reflectors (see Figure 3.2 in Chapter 3). The nuclear explosion sends out high-energy X-rays, a portion of which enter the rods and strip the electrons out of atoms in the fiber, producing ionized ions. At the high temperatures present in the nuclear explosion, on average only a single electron remains bound in the electron shells of the atom. Such a mono-electron ion is called a hydrogenic ion.

Certain hydrogenic ions have metastable (long-lived) excited energy levels that the electron can occupy. Such ions are candidates for use in the fiber since they provide a means for achieving a population inversion: The electrons stay in this metastable energy state for a time, but when they decay to the next lower energy state, they stay in that state for a much briefer period of time, quickly decaying to an even lower energy state (generally the ground state). Thus, on average there is a population inversion with more atoms with electrons in the metastable state than in the lower state that the electron first decays to. X-ray laser development uses atoms whose hydrogenic ions have good metastable-excited states.

One can understand how X-ray frequencies f are achieved by looking at the energy levels the remaining bound electron can occupy in the hydrogenic ion. Their difference would be the energy emitted E (directly proportional to the frequency) for a transition from orbital level n_1 to n_2. This is the same as for a normal hydrogen ion, except for the atomic number Z (number of protons) for the atom used in the laser:

$$\begin{aligned}
E(n_2, n_1) &= (Z^2 m_e e^4/2h^2)(1/n_1{}^2 - 1/n_2{}^2) \\
&= 13.6 \ eV \ Z^2(1/n_1{}^2 - 1/n_2{}^2) \\
&= hf
\end{aligned}$$

where h is the Planck's constant, e the charge of the electron, and f the frequency of the emitted radiation.

The laser mechanism was independently analyzed by Soviet physicists, who identified the metastable states of zinc or copper as appropriate for an X-ray laser.[1] Lasers using these metals would lase at a wavelength of around 14 Å. (One Å is one-hundred millionth of a centimeter.) An analysis of the electron transitions for an X-ray laser using a hydrogenic zinc ion, along with characteristic laser parameters, is contained in Ritson.[2]

X-ray-laser experiments performed at Lawrence Livermore Laboratory and the Princeton Plasma Physics Laboratory have shown that large gains can be achieved by selenium fibers and that somewhat smaller but significant gains can be achieved by carbon.[3] These latter elements lase at longer wavelengths in a range that is called the extreme ultraviolet (on the borderline to the X-ray range.) Later reports on these experiments indicated that the Lawrence Livermore results were probably in error, but there is little doubt that lasing occurred in these experiments.[4]

One can determine how much more intense the X-rays at a distance will be for the X-ray laser than for a normal nuclear explosion. Basically the laser directs part of the X-ray energy toward the target rather than having all of it spread out uniformly in a sphere as with a normal nuclear explosion. Thus the energy density U that is achieved at the missiles is:

$$U = \frac{W}{4\pi r^2} \times \frac{4\pi\epsilon}{\pi(\theta/2)^2} = \frac{4\epsilon W}{\pi\theta^2 r^2}$$

The first term is just the spreading of the energy density, and the second term is the laser gain G caused by the intensifying of the radiation created by confining it to a small angle θ rather than the whole solid angle 4π, with the efficiency of conversion of the bomb energy to the laser energy denoted as ϵ. Here r is the distance of the target from the nuclear X-ray-laser explosion, and W is the explosive energy of the nuclear device. Figure A6.1 shows the origin of the first term in the way the energy density of a nuclear explosion spreads, and Figure A6.2 illustrates the origin of G (the second term).

The angle of divergence θ depends on the diffraction-limited angle $1.22\ \lambda/d$ and the geometric divergence angle d/L (caused by the finite length L of the lasing rod), where d is the diameter of the rod and L the length. Then θ is given by

$$\theta = [(1.22\lambda/d)^2 + (d/L)^2]^{1/2}$$

The width of the rod d can be chosen in terms of the length L by using a simple variational principle to minimize the divergence angle (taking the

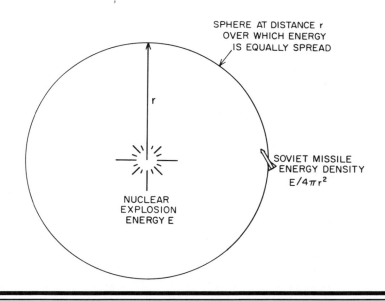

Fig. A6.1. The density of the energy of a nuclear explosion a distance r away assuming the energy is distributed isotropically over the sphere at radius r.

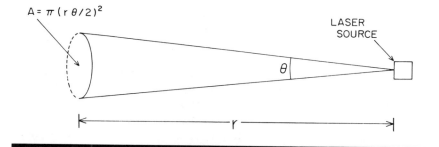

Fig. A6.2. Cone formed by an expanding laser beam from a source. The surface area of the sphere ($4\pi r^2$) over area A of the beam gives the angular factor in the gain.

derivative of θ with respect to d and setting it equal to 0). This was first done in Walbridge:[5]

$$d_{min} = (1.22\lambda L)^{1/2}$$
$$\theta_{min} = (2.44\lambda/L)^{1/2}$$

For a typical example of the conditions for a minimum divergence angle and the gain achievable, assume

$$L = 2\ m$$
$$\epsilon = 1\%$$
$$\lambda = 14\ \text{Å}$$

The minimum angle of divergence, laser rod width, and gain is then

$$d_{min} = 58.4\ \mu m$$
$$\theta_{min} = 4.13 \times 10^{-5}\ \text{radians}$$
$$G = 0.94 \times 10^8$$

The gain G indicates the huge increase in the energy intensity of the X-rays in the beam path over that of an ordinary nuclear explosion. It occurs because the bomb power that goes into the laser is highly directional. This allows for much higher intensities in the direction of the laser beam, which would be necessary to kill missiles. This huge gain is the reason for the military attraction of this device.

Because of the enormous increase in the destructive energy available from these and similar devices using a nuclear explosion as the energy source over that of a simple nuclear explosion, they are known as third-generation nuclear weapons.[6] The potential offensive use of these devices is much greater than their potential defensive uses, as discussed in Chapters 8 and 9. The X-ray laser has been designated as "a weapon for the twenty-first century" because of its potential as an offensive weapon.[7]

Research and development of these weapons has been carried out through the use of underground nuclear explosions. Chapter 10 points out that developing these weapons for a ballistic-missile defense (or an anti-satellite weapon) will require testing in space, which would violate both the 1967 Treaty on Principles Governing the Activities of States in the Exploration of Outer Space and the 1972 ABM Treaty.

Rise Height and Fuel Required for an X-Ray-Laser Boost-Phase Defense

One can determine the minimum rise height and fuel required for submarine-based X-ray-laser rockets to be able to hit the missiles over the Earth's curvature and atmosphere by using the basic geometry shown in Figure A7.1. The submarines are assumed to be based in the Indian Ocean, the location of the closest approach to most of the ICBM targets. The ICBMs are assumed to take off at their present launch angle of 23°, chosen to minimize the fuel needed for the missiles. As discussed in Chapter 6 and shown in Appendix 13, this could be lowered and the boost-phase time shortened with fast-burn boosters and larger fuel tanks to end the boost phase inside the atmosphere. The case that the Soviets have not developed that capability will be examined here.

The X-ray-laser beam cannot penetrate the atmosphere below about 100 kilometers (except for bleaching at high altitudes), so the line between it and the missile it targets generally has to be above that. The model in Figure A7.1 is one for a minimum height for the X-ray-laser rocket to hit the target by the end of the boost phase, with the X-ray beam taken to be just above (grazing) the atmosphere at its closest approach. The height of the atmosphere will be taken to be 100 kilometers.

The time required for the X-ray-laser rocket to rise to the height necessary to hit the missile can be minimized by choosing the appropriate angle of launch of the rocket. A line has been drawn out radially from the Earth that intersects the line from the target grazing the atmosphere. The rocket can target the missile when it reaches this line, and it is obvious that the shortest distance for the rocket to travel to this line occurs for an arrival perpendicular to the line (as a variational calculation could show).

Assume the height of the top of the atmosphere is h, the distance the

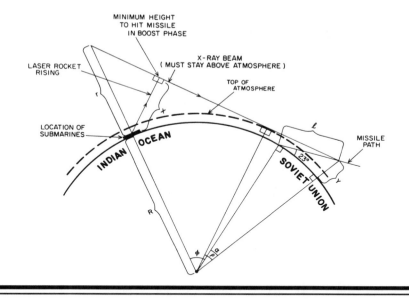

Fig. A7.1. Geometry of launching of an X-ray laser to the minimum height necessary for the laser beam to be able to pass over the atmosphere and hit the missile in its boost phase.

missile has traveled when it is first subjected to a hit by the X-ray laser is l, the height which the X-ray laser must reach to hit the missile is x, and the angle with respect to the center of the Earth at which the missile launch sight is to the submarines which will launch the X-ray laser is φ.

Extra lines have been drawn from the center of the Earth, one to the point where the ICBM is when the X-ray laser first hits it (of length $R + y$, where $R = 6,377$ kilometers is the Earth's radius), and one to the point where the X-ray-laser beam is just tangent to the upper atmosphere (of length $R + h$). The angle the two lines form with each other is denoted by ϱ, and the angle the first line forms with the line drawn from the Earth's center to the launch site of the missile is denoted by α. Simple geometry shows that the angle of launch for the rocket is $\varphi - (\varrho - \alpha)$. Using basic trigonometric rules for the four triangles in the diagram — three with one vertex at the Earth's center (two of them are obviously right triangles), and one right triangle with the missile launch site as one vertex and the missile in the target range a second vertex — we have the following relationships:

$$l = y/\sin 23° = 2.56\, y \tag{1}$$

$$\cos \varrho = (R + h)/(R + y) \tag{2}$$

$$l^2 = R^2 + (R + y)^2 - 2R(R + y)\cos \alpha \tag{3}$$

$$\cos [\varphi - (\varrho - \alpha)] = (R + h)/(R + r) \tag{4}$$

$$x = r \cos [\varphi - (\varrho - \alpha)] \tag{5}$$

Equations (4) and (5) allow an elimination of r:

$$x = R \{1 - \cos [\varphi - (\varrho - \alpha)]\} + h \tag{6}$$

The distance z that the beam must travel before it hits the missile once it is fired from the X-ray laser rocket is given by

$$z = (R + h - x) \tan[\varphi - (\varrho - \alpha)] + (R + h) \tan \varrho \tag{7}$$

The above equations can be used to calculate the minimum height and final velocity for the X-ray-laser rocket that will be required in order for the rocket to reach the required altitude in sufficient time to destroy a substantial portion of the missiles in the boost phase. This can then be used to determine the ratio of the mass of the fuel required to power the rocket to the mass of the X-ray-laser payload that must be delivered to the appropriate height, similar to the calculation in Bethe and Garwin[1]. This is done through the standard rocket equation of motion:

$$m\, dv/dt = v_e\, dm/dt + mg - \beta v \tag{8}$$

where m is the mass of the rocket, v its velocity and β the frictional coefficient. The first term on the right-hand side is the exhaust velocity v_e multiplying the rate of change of the mass, the second the gravitational attraction on the rocket, and the third air friction. The first term is much larger than the second two, so the latter terms will be neglected. (This approximation slightly underestimates the fuel mass required.) Then equation (8) integrates to the form

$$m_f/m_i = \exp(v_f/v_e) \tag{9}$$

where m_i is the initial mass (payload + fuel) and m_f and v_f are the final rocket (payload) mass and velocity. Knowing the exhaust velocity for the fuel and the final velocity of the missile required for it to reach the required height in time for a boost-phase defense, one can determine the ratio of the initial mass (fuel plus payload) for the missile to the final mass (payload) of the X-ray rocket.

For a boost-phase defense the rocket must achieve a high rate of acceleration to reach the heights required in the short time available. The greatest acceleration is produced by chemical engines, which generally have an exhaust velocity of around 3 kilometers per second and can potentially only produce a maximum exhaust velocity of around 5 kilometers per second. We will assume the latter can be achieved for an X-ray-laser rocket.

To simplify the problem, the rocket acceleration will be assumed to be a constant. The time allowed for detecting the missile launch, alerting, and preparing the rocket for attack will be taken as 30 seconds. Then $x = at_r^2$ is the height to which the rocket can rise and target the missile in time $t_r = t_b - 30$ seconds, where t_b is the boost-phase time for the missiles. Thus for $t_b = 180$ seconds, available in Soviet SS-24s and SS-25s, $t_r = 150$ seconds. The Soviets can install fast-burn boosters on their missiles to achieve shorter boost-phase times and should easily be able to achieve a 150-second boost-phase time without fast-burn boosters.

Table A7.1 contains results for the minimum height necessary and the minimum mass ratio necessary to reach that height in the time available for φ in the range for southernmost Soviet ICBM fields. If the payload of the rocket has a mass of 1,000 kilograms (just over a ton), the fuel required for the missile is 18,000 kilograms (about 20 tons) for the most optimum case (countering the most southern Soviet missiles in the case of 150-second boost-phase time). This corresponds to a rocket weight about 50% larger than current submarine missiles. However, the other cases are all orders of magnitude larger than what a submarine could carry and launch, particularly for boost-phase times shorter than 150 seconds. In general, the rockets with the required conditions necessary for a boost-phase intercept cannot be built for submarine basing.

These calculations show that the X-ray laser based on submarines cannot be used as a boost-phase defense.

Table A7.1. Height and mass ratios required for interception

φ	t_b (sec)	y (km)	ϱ	α	x (km)	m_i/m_f
35°	80	129	5.4°	2.7°	1,090	6,124
35°	100	160	7.8°	3.3°	986	280
35°	150	232	11.5°	4.8°	865	18
40°	80	129	5.4°	2.7°	1,409	78,590
40°	100	160	7.8°	3.3°	1,290	1,588
40°	150	232	11.5°	4.8°	1,151	47
45°	80	129	5.4°	2.7°	1,766	1.42×10^6
45°	100	160	7.8°	3.3°	1,633	11,269
45°	150	232	11.5°	4.8°	1,477	138

APPENDIX 8

How the Excimer Laser Works

Excimer lasers are a type of existing laser that could be used with the orbiting-mirror proposal for a boost-phase defense (described in Chapter 3). Because the laser operates in the ultraviolet, which penetrates the atmosphere with only a 10%–20% loss of power, it is appropriate for this type of defense. Using the laser in a ground-based mode makes regular maintenance of the laser a much easier task.

Excimer lasers have a lasing medium that consists of diatomic molecules in which one atom is a noble gas and the other atom is a halogen. Examples are xenon fluoride (XeF) and krypton fluoride (KrF). These diatomic molecules are not stable. When electrons in an upper molecular energy state decay into the ground state, the energy released by the transition is more than adequate to break the weak chemical bond of the molecule, and the molecule dissociates.

The molecular dissociation tends to maintain a natural population inversion, since there are always so few molecules in the lower state compared to the number in the upper state at any given time, given the rapid rate of dissociation of molecules after a transition to the ground state. Most of the energy given up by electron decay goes into breaking the molecular bond of the molecule. The rest is emitted as a photon in the ultraviolet. The maximum efficiency of the laser is generally around 6%. Most excimer lasers today have efficiencies around 1%.

A more technical overview of excimer lasers under research for a possible strategic defense is in the American Physical Society report.[1]

How the Free-Electron Laser Works

The free-electron laser consists of a beam of electrons moving at velocities near the speed of light, passing through a region with a sinusoidal spatially varying magnetic field. (See Figure A9.1 for a configuration of the free-electron laser.) The electron beam moves around in an ellipse using the "racetrack" configuration. In the interaction region the spacing of the spatial magnetic oscillations is set equal to the wavelength of the radiation λ desired (corrected by a relativistic factor q). The rapidly moving electrons discern the magnetic field oscillations as an electromagnetic wave in their rest frame. This interaction causes the beam to emit some of the energy of its motion in the form of radiation.

Development of the lasing section takes into account that as energy of the beam is emitted in the form of radiation, its resonant wavelength increases because the kinetic energy of the beam is lowered. Thus for continuous emission across the interaction region, the spacing of oscillations of the magnetic field should also continually decrease to maintain resonance and emission. Variation of the spacing of the magnetic oscillations to maintain resonance with the electron beam converts more energy of the laser into radiation and emits a narrow spectrum of in-phase waves in the ultraviolet.

The efficiency of the conversion of electron beam energy to radiation depends not only on the wavelength of operation and the length over which resonance is maintained but also on the relativistic factor of the electrons. As the electrons approach the speed of light, this factor rises rapidly. Thus, to develop high-powered electron lasers needed for this defense, the electrons must be accelerated up to very high energies at speeds very close to that of light.

On the other side of the racetrack is the region where reacceleration occurs. Once part of the energy of the particles in the beam in their very rapid motion have gone into the radiation emitted, they are moving more slowly than before and have to be speeded up to their previous velocity before reentering the lasing section. Almost all of the energy that goes into the laser goes into this particle-acceleration region, which accelerates the electron beam back up to the same velocity to reenter the lasing section.

Research on this laser will very likely enable the production of high-powered lasers with frequencies in the ultraviolet, the range desired to use them for ground-based laser-beam sources in the orbiting-mirror defense.

The report of the American Physical Society study has a technical discussion of the characteristics of free-electron lasers undergoing research.[1]

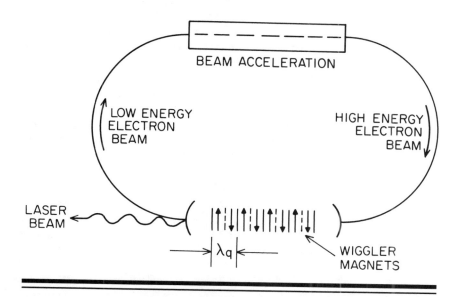

Fig. A9.1. The basic structure of a free-electron laser in the racetrack configuration, showing the reacceleration region for the electron beam and the lasing region where a periodically varying magnetic field causes the electron beam to emit the radiation that makes up the beam.

Power Levels Required for the Orbiting-Mirror Defense

There are several potential difficulties with the proposal for a boost-phase defense using ground-based lasers and mirror reflectors around the Earth. Some of these problems involve the phenomena that can occur in the Earth's atmosphere to degrade the laser beam. Atmospheric turbulence will cause the beam to spread out and wander in a random fashion. Much of this could be corrected (with the exception of rapid turbulent changes much shorter than a second) if appropriate adoptive optics are developed, such as by optical phase conjugation using a low-powered return beam from the mirror. The phenomenon of "thermal blooming" will cause an expansion of the beam. This involves the heating of the air that the beam passes through, with a subsequent expansion of the heated air, which pulls the laser beam with it. The laser beam can also ionize the atmosphere in the beam path (by knocking out the outer electrons of the atmospheric molecules), and this ionization process will absorb energy from the beam. Water vapor and dust in the atmosphere can absorb energy from the laser beam, decreasing the amount of power that reaches the mirror.

The problem of sending a high-power beam up to a geosynchronous mirror and reflecting it down to the low-Earth-orbit mirrors has serious difficulties, even ignoring the problem of the degradation of the beam in the Earth's atmosphere. One ground-based station will not be sufficient, because a cloudy day would disable a laser site. Clouds absorb the energy of the beam, significantly reducing its power. Attempting to burn a hole in the cloud will not work since clouds are almost always moving with respect to the ground and will continually diffuse into and fill up that hole. Thus several laser stations placed throughout the United States will be needed, so that there will be a few that are not in an overcast area. (Even then, there will be a small but finite probability that all of them are cloud-covered.)

To determine the minimum requirements of energy for those lasers to destroy missiles, one must determine the energy that strikes the missiles after going through the atmosphere, reflecting off a mirror out at 22,000 miles from the Earth, and reflecting off the low-orbiting mirrors onto the missiles. The total energy of the laser beam that must reach the missiles by this circuitous route is the energy fluence at the missile target J, times the area of the beam spot A, times the number of missiles M. All of this energy will not end up upon the missiles being targeted, so the actual amount will be corrected by the efficiencies of the laser, the transmission through the atmosphere, and the delivery of the energy to the target. Thus this product must be equal to the total energy E_{total} used to power the lasers, the lasers multiplied by the efficiency of the laser ϵ_{laser}, the efficiency of transmission through the atmosphere ϵ_{trans}, and the efficiency of with which the energy reaches the target ϵ_{dest}. Thus

$$\epsilon_{dest} \; \epsilon_{laser} \; \epsilon_{trans} \; E_{total} \; = \; MJA$$

Sources capable of generating E_{total} must be available at each ground laser site.

The minimum needed energy fluence to destroy the missile J is about 10 kilojoules per square centimeter (from Appendix 3). The laser efficiency of free-electron lasers for the defense will be assumed to be 25% (excimer lasers are much less efficient). The number of missiles M will be assumed to be the present number of Soviet ICBMs of 1,400 (the Soviets will undoubtedly have greater number by the time of deployment). The area of the laser spot A can be determined through the angle of divergence of the laser beam and the distance r over which the beam travels (22,000 miles or 36,000 kilometers). The angle of divergence θ_{dl} depends on the mirror diameter d of the mirror and the wavelength λ of the laser. The operational wavelength of the laser will be taken to be $\lambda \cong 0.3$ microns. Assuming (optimistically) that 10-meter diameter mirrors will be used, then

$$\theta_{dl} = 1.22 \; \lambda/d = 3.7 \times 10^{-8} \text{ radians}$$
$$A = \pi(r\theta_{dl}/2)^2 = 1.47 \text{ m}^2$$

Assume that most of the energy loss in the air is due to Rayleigh scattering (Rayleigh scattering of the sunlight causes the sky to be blue) and ignore all other factors causing energy loss. At sea level, 90% of the energy will be lost due to this scattering, but assume that the laser station is put upon a mountain 2 miles high to reduce that amount to 80%.[1] Then $\epsilon_{trans} = 0.2$. Assume $\epsilon_{laser} = 0.25$ for a free-electron laser. The value of ϵ_{dest} is the most difficult to estimate. For a beam that travels over 40,000 miles, a substantial amount of power will be lost before it reaches the secondary mirrors, even if the targeting of the missiles from those secondary mirrors is quite accurate so that little energy is lost in this process. A very optimistic value of $\epsilon_{dest} = 0.2$ will be assumed.

The minimum amount of energy that would be needed is then

$$E_{total} = 2.1 \times 10^{13} \text{ joules}$$

Taking the Soviet missile boost phase time to be 100 seconds, this translates into a power consumption rate of

$$P_{total} = 2.1 \times 10^{11} \text{ watts}$$

For comparison, this power is about equal the to the power consumption of the entire United States.

If there is an average 20% chance of cloudiness at the laser sites, then five laser stations on the ground will be needed have a 99.9% chance that one will be usable, while if the average chance of cloudiness is 50%, 10 laser stations will be needed to give a 99.9% chance of at least one being available. Note that there will always be rare periods when all stations are cloudy.

We can estimate the minimum cost of this power if we use the minimum cost power generation from nuclear reactors (the cheapest source today). That is $1,000 per kilowatt, so this defense energy source has a minimum cost of $210 billion. That is $150 million per missile destroyed by the defense, about 6 times the cost of the missile itself, at about $25 million.

Less expensive power generators may be built in the future, such as magnetohydrodynamic generators that are under research. But even if this is the case, remember that this calculation is for a minimum on the amount of power that would be required for the generator, assuming that certain conditions would be achievable: that laser stations with high efficiencies could be constructed; that large, accurate, and efficient mirrors could be built; that a high percentage of the laser energy strikes the missiles; that the Soviets would not attack the mirrors with antisatellite weapons; and that a critical malfunction would not reduce the system's capabilities (this may be particularly critical at the geosynchronous mirror).

It is worth considering just one of these effects in more detail: the accuracy of the laser beam from the Earth necessary to reach the geosynchronous mirror. This is a critical problem because so much can happen in the atmosphere to throw the beam off course. In fact, for a 10-meter geosynchronous mirror, the beam direction angle has to be accurate to a value within 1.4×10^{-7} radians to hit the mirror! That means that when the beam has traveled 1 kilometer, it has to be accurate to within 0.01 centimeter, or when it has traveled 10 kilometers (6.2 miles), it has to be accurate to within 0.1 centimeter! Even with optics of this accuracy, any minor atmospheric effect that disturbs the beam (e.g., refraction by water droplets) can cause a larger error than this. Furthermore, potential errors can be induced in the geosynchronous mirror reflecting the very high-powered beams required for the defense. This high-powered reflection will severely heat the mirror, so major cooling systems will be required to reduce the distortion this heating can cause. However, even with the cooling systems, distortions that result in significant errors will likely occur. Thus, just generating a laser beam with this precision will be a major task requiring advanced future technology!

Power Required for a Neutral-Beam Defense

Neutral beams are undergoing serious research for a later-phase space-based defense. Difficulties and countermeasures they face, such as counters with high-altitude nuclear explosions (analyzed in Appendix 12) were mentioned in Chapters 3 and 6. An important question is how much power will be required for a low-Earth-orbit defense using neutral particle beams to counter the missiles.

The nature of the destruction by particle beams differs from that of lasers because particle beams penetrate deep into their target rather than destroying the surface as lasers do. (For this reason missiles cannot be shielded from particle beams as they could from lasers.) The value for the energy density necessary to destroy a missile in the boost phase is generally a few hundred joules per gram in the target. If we take a minimum energy concentration of 200 joules per gram (the limit to detonate the missile fuel or the explosives in the warhead) and take a minimum depth for this deposition of 0.1 meters, then the energy fluence necessary for an aluminum missile (of density 2.7 g/cm³) is $J = 5$ kJ/cm². This minimum lethality criterion was the value determined in the recent American Physical Society study.[1] The required energy density will be denoted as W in the following equation.

The total energy that will be expended using neutral beams to take out the missiles in the boost phase is then

$$E_{total} = MJA/\epsilon_{acc}\epsilon_{dest}$$

where M is the number of missiles to be taken out, A is the average cross-sectional area of the particle beam after traveling the distance from the source to the rocket, ϵ_{acc} is the efficiency of the accelerator in converting input energy into the energy of the accelerated beam, and ϵ_{dest} is the efficiency with which energy emitted in the neutral beam goes into destruction of the missiles. A can be determined from the divergence angle for the beam. If one assumes that 500 MeV energies can be obtained for a beam of neutral hydrogen atoms, the divergence angle (diffraction limited) is θ_{dl} $= 1.4 \times 10^{-6}$ radians (the divergence angle does not become much larger for more modest beam energies).[2] Hence if the typical distance of the missiles from the defense station is 1,000 kilometers, then

$$A = \pi(r\theta_{dl}/2)^2 = 1.57 \text{ m}^2$$

Assume that the number of missiles is the present number of Soviet ICBMs of 1,400 (a number which the Soviets will expand for reasons discussed in the text), ϵ_{acc} is 10%, ϵ_{dest} is 25%, and $W = 5$ kJ/cm². Then

$$E_{total} = 4.2 \times 10^{12} \text{ joules}$$

Assume that after the missile emerges from the atmosphere, there are 50 seconds left in the boost phase for it to be used in targeting and destroying the missiles. Then the power needed for this time is

$$P = 8.4 \times 10^{10} \text{ watts}$$

For comparison, this is about 40% of the rate of power consumption of the United States.

The present minimum cost for generating this much power is $1,000 per kilowatt, so the cost of the estimated power requirements would be about $84 billion at these rates ($60 million for every $25-million missile taken out). Cheaper power sources can probably be developed, but the Soviets can also build more missiles and can reduce the boost-phase time during which the missile is available for attack by the defense. These factors could significantly increase the power required. Furthermore, since this defense can be based only on satellites, there will have to be several satellites for every one that is over the Soviet missile fields, further multiplying the potential power sources needed by the absentee ratio. With this defense, it costs an order of magnitude more to take out each missile than the actual cost of the missile. (In addition, the cost of building and launching the accelerators adds substantially to the cost of the destructive power generation.)

The high energies that the beams of each satellite will have to be accelerated to in order to deliver this much total energy with only a few hundred satellites will be on the 100-megawatt level (requiring a billion-watt power source). Current high-"energy" particle accelerators (i.e., accelerators that make the very small particles attain high energies) operate on very low current and are thus still low powered. It is unlikely for a 100-megawatt accelerator to be built in the near future that is small enough that one could launch it into space with even the heavy lift launcher. In any case, the cost for this defense, just as for the mirror defense, will likely be another expensive item that this country cannot afford.

Countermeasure of a High-Altitude Nuclear Blast

One countermeasure that could be effective against the particle-beam interceptor and could seriously debilitate other schemes for the defense is a high-altitude nuclear explosion. The nuclear-explosion blast wave in the area above the Soviet Union would send enough pressure hundreds of kilometers into the surrounding area to ensure that rapid scattering of high-energy particles sent out into that area in a particle beam would occur. Furthermore, the energy of the collisions of the neutral particles in the beam with atmospheric particles will cause the neutral particles to break up into charged particles again. Thus magnetic-field effects would deflect them away from their target.

To see how effective the use of a nuclear explosion would be, one can use an empirical formula that has been developed from nuclear-explosion experiments for the pressure (in psi) behind the shock front created by the blast wave as a function of the distance away from the blast:[1]

$$P = 155.5 \ W^{2/3}/r^2$$

where W is the explosive force in megatons and r is the distance from the explosive center in kilometers. Assume a $W = 1$ megaton. One can then calculate the mean free path of the particles on the beam (the distance which the particle will travel before having a collision, at which point it is taken out of useful action), which is proportional to $1/P$. For neutral-hydrogen atoms at atmospheric pressure, this mean free path is 8.8×10^{-5} meters. Thus we have the following mean free paths (mfp) at distances from the explosions:

$$
\text{mfp} = \begin{cases}
8.3 \text{ meters at } r = 1{,}000 \text{ kilometers} \\
33.2 \text{ meters at } r = 2{,}000 \text{ kilometers} \\
74.9 \text{ meters at } r = 3{,}000 \text{ kilometers}
\end{cases}
$$

However, the beam particles would need a mean free path of several hundred kilometers to be able to destroy a significant number of the boost-phase missiles. Thus the effect of the explosion is to nullify the particle beam when the shock front reaches the defense.

The nuclear-explosion countermeasure can also be useful in countering other defense techniques. In the X-ray-laser defense, the radiation gets absorbed in a thin layer in the upper atmosphere. A high-altitude nuclear-explosion countermeasure would send an atmospheric protection out for hundreds of kilometers, which would absorb part of the energy of the X-ray-laser radiation, reducing its ability to counter missiles or warheads.

In the case of the orbiting-mirror defense, there are a number of ways a nuclear explosion could be used to counter it. In addition to direct attacks on the geosynchronous mirror and low-altitude orbiting mirrors, the Soviets could have satellites with nuclear explosives in low Earth orbits that covered the general vicinity above the Soviet Union, to be exploded upon shortly before the launch of the missiles. This would interfere with the transfer of the laser beam from the geosynchronous mirror, significantly reducing its effectiveness at taking out the missiles.

In addition to the problems to the defense that would be created by the blast wave of the high-altitude nuclear explosion, the electromagnetic pulse and beta blackout created by the explosion would severely hamper the defense system's detection and tracking mechanism. As discussed in Chapter 6, there are several ways a nuclear explosion could be used as a countermeasure against a ballistic-missile defense.

Dynamics of Ending the Missile Boost Phase in the Atmosphere

An effective countermeasure to boost-phase defenses involving certain types of chemical lasers, X-ray lasers, particle beams, homing rockets, and even Brilliant Pebbles is to end the boost phase "inside the atmosphere." The atmospheric pressure is actually continually decreasing with height, but for the purpose of avoiding these boost-phase defenses, it is safe to assume the atmosphere lies at altitudes above the Earth's surface up to 100 kilometers. Bleaching of the atmosphere might allow laser-beam penetration down to 80 kilometers altitude, whereas particle beams cannot effectively penetrate below about 150 kilometers.

In order to end the boost phase in the atmosphere, a missile must have a fast-burn booster. To facilitate the process, it would help to lower the launch angle for the missile below its present optimum of 23°, the value that is chosen to minimize the amount of fuel spent (lowering the launch angle would require the installation of larger fuel tanks). One can calculate what the Soviets need to be able to do this by determining how short the boost-phase time needs to be if the present optimum angle is maintained or if the angle is lowered by using larger fuel tanks.

The acceleration of the missile increases in time during the boost phase, since the mass of the rocket decreases as fuel is burned. This is given by the equation of motion, which can be integrated (see Appendix 7):

$$m \, dv/dt = -v_e \, dm/dt$$
$$m(t)/m_i = \exp[-v(t)/v_e] \tag{1}$$

where m is the mass of the missile, having value m_i at the launch and m_b at

187

the end of the boost phase; v is the rocket velocity having the value of v_b at the end of the boost phase. The missile exhaust velocity is v_e.

The value of dm/dt will be taken to be constant, since the fuel burns at an approximately constant rate. Thus $m(t)$ is linearly decreasing in t, and the rate of decrease can be expressed in terms of m_b and t_b, the boost-phase time. This determines the velocity in equation (1), and integration determines the height as a function of time. At the end of the boost phase, the height h_b is given by

$$h_b = \{v_e - v_b/[\exp(v_b/v_e) - 1]\}\, t_b \tag{2}$$

The term v_b can be determined by the fact that the total (kinetic plus potential) energy of the rocket must remain the same when it reaches it maximum height h_{max} in its whole course of flight to the United States, at which point the velocity is zero and it has only a gravitational potential. Because h_{max} is significant compared to the radius R of the Earth, the curved-Earth forms of potential energy should be used. We have

$$mv_b^2/2 - mMG/(R + h_b) = -mMG/(R + h_{max})$$
$$v_b = [2MG(h_{max} - h_b)/(R + h_{max})(R + h_b)]^{1/2} \tag{3}$$

The expression $MG/R^2 = g = 9.8$ m/s² is just the gravitational acceleration rate at the Earth's surface. For ICBMs, $h_{max} = 1{,}200$ kilometers. Take $h_b = 100$ kilometers as the effective height of the atmosphere (for example, for the X-ray laser, over 90% of the laser energy has been scattered out of a beam penetrating down to this height, while for a particle-beam weapon, well over 99% of it has been scattered after it penetrates down to this height). Then (3) yields

$$v_b = 4{,}210 \text{ m/s} \tag{4}$$

From Equation (2), the specification of h_b and v_b determines t_b; $v_e = 3$ km/s for ballistic missiles. Hence the time from the launch to the atmosphere exit is

$$t_b = 61.4 \text{ seconds} \tag{5}$$

Thus a boost-phase time of 61 seconds is required to end the boost phase inside the atmosphere at 100 kilometers height or below. To avoid bleaching of the atmosphere that might allow laser-beam penetration to 80 kilometers' altitude, a 49-second boost-phase time would be required.

To end the boost phase at 150 kilometers, which would effectively escape a particle-beam defense, the missile parameters are

$$v_b = 4,088 \text{ m/s}$$
$$t_b = 94.1 \text{ seconds} \qquad (6)$$

Thus a 94-second boost-phase time is necessary for avoiding a particle-beam defense.

The above calculations assume a launch at the currently set 23° angle, which gives the peak height h_{max} of 1,200 kilometers. However, if larger fuel tanks are installed, the missiles could be launched at a smaller angle, relaxing the boost-phase time required for ending in the atmosphere. Since v_b is the radial velocity for a 23° launch, then the total velocity of the missile at the end of the boost phase is equal to 4,210/ sin 23° = 10,776 meters/second. Thus if a launch is made at an angle of only 15°, the boost-phase time can be lengthened. For that angle the radial velocity and time at the end of the boost phase ending at 100 kilometers altitude are

$$v_b = 10,776 \sin 15° \text{ m/s} = 2,789 \text{ m/s}$$
$$t_b = 84.6 \text{ seconds} \qquad (7)$$

Thus the effect of lowering the launch angle to 15° increases the boost-phase time to 84 seconds for ending the boost phase in the atmosphere at an altitude under 100 kilometers. The boost-phase time for ending the boost phase at 150 kilometers is 130 seconds. For comparison, the boost-phase time of many current U.S. ICBMs (launched at 23°) is 150 seconds.

The boost-phase times for ending at the two altitudes discussed are summarized in Table A13.1. With fast-burn boosters, the Soviets can probably develop boost-phase times as short as 40–50 seconds by the early part of the next century, so they may develop the capacity to end the boost phase in the atmosphere even without lowering the angle of their launch. Then boost-phase defenses using chemical lasers at frequencies that do not penetrate the atmosphere, X-ray lasers, particle beams, homing rockets, and Brilliant Pebbles would be rendered virtually useless.

Table A13.1. Times for ending a missile boost phase in the atmosphere

Height (km)	Launch Angle	Boost-Phase Times (sec)
80	23°	49
100	23°	61
150	23°	94
80	15°	67
100	15°	84
150	15°	130

From Public Law 99-145: Requirements for Strategic Defense Deployment

This provision was passed by Congress as part (Sec. 222) of the Department of Defense Authorization Act of 1986:

A strategic defense system developed as a consequence of research, development, test, and evaluation conducted on the Strategic Defense Initiative program may not be deployed in whole or in part unless —

(1) the President determines and certifies to Congress in writing that —

    (A) the system is survivable (that is, the system is able to maintain a sufficient degree of effectiveness to fulfill its mission, even in the face of determined attacks against it); and

    (B) the system is cost effective at the margin to the extent that the system is able to maintain its defense at less cost than it would take to develop offensive countermeasures and proliferate the ballistic missiles necessary to overcome it; and

(2) funding for the deployment of such system has been specifically authorized by legislation enacted after the date on which the President makes the certification to Congress.

Source: *United States Statutes at Large,* vol. 99 (1985).

Requirements for Space-Based Interceptors in a Boost-Phase Defense

Like the question on the number of satellites required for a space-based laser defense, the question on the number of satellites required for a space-based boost-phase interceptor (SBI) planned for Phase I deployment needs to be determined. Like the problem of the number of laser satellites required, this depends on the number of missiles the Soviets have deployed, the configuration of the satellites, and the boost-phase time for the missiles.

This problem was addressed in a 1988 paper by David Spergel and George Field. They considered the case that the Soviets stationed five local fields of 250 new ICBMs each year (using the Soviet 1980 rate of new missile buildup) such as SS-24s and SS-25s, at a given northern latitude, with the radius of the fields taken to be 200 kilometers. They determined the number of interceptors that would be required each year for a boost-phase defense against those missiles.[1]

SS-25s were estimated to cost about $50 million apiece when the costs of operations and maintenance for the missiles are included. These have a 180-second boost-phase time. Thus the yearly cost of adding 250 new SS-25s would be $12.5 billion. In response to deployment of SBIs, the Soviets may switch to fast-burn booster deployment. A fast-burn booster was estimated to cost a maximum of $90 million and possibly much less, even significantly less than an SS-25. The yearly costs of fast-burn boosters would be a maximum of $22.5 billion.

On the other hand, the number of SBIs N in the boost-phase force needed to counter the missiles added each year for different boost-phase times t_b, determined by Spergel and Fields, is shown in Table A15.1. Using the Marshall Institute estimate of $6 million for each SBI (which may be

191

too low), the cost for the SBI defense is estimated. The $6 million per interceptor estimate does not include the cost of deployment and maintaining the defense, so a comparison will be made between the cost for the defense with the cost of the missiles. Without the fast-burn boosters (180-second boost-phase time or a future 150-second boost-phase time), the yearly defense costs are 3–5 times as expensive as the offensive missile costs. With fast-burn booster added, that cost ratio of defense to offense increases to a minimum of 8 if the boost-phase time is reduced to 90 seconds, or a minimum of 13 if the boost phase is reduced to 75 seconds. A 60-second boost-phase time avoids the SBI defense entirely.

Table A15.1. SBIs required to counter missiles for various boost-phase times

t_b (sec)	Absentee Ratio	N	Cost ($ billion)
60		inaccessible	
75	121	48,000	300
90	76	30,000	180
120	38	15,000	90
150	24	9,600	58
180	18	7,000	42

The Marshall Institute estimates that SBIs can be 90% effective in hitting their targets. Without effective battle-management capabilities (which may not be available for a Phase I defense), the targeting will be random, and the overall effectiveness in taking the missile force is reduced to 76%. However, in realistic battle conditions with well-developed decoys, the SBIs will probably be at most 50% effective in hitting their targets. Without well-coordinated target assignments from battle management, the overall effectiveness will be even less. The ERIS and HEDI interceptors will have to attack the leakage in the midcourse and terminal layers.

The much greater cost of the defense over the offense holds for Phase I deployment as well as for latter phases, even though the effectiveness of the Phase I defense is very doubtful, as discussed in Chapter 7. Like the later phases of defense planned, it can be overwhelmed by a significant offensive buildup.

The 1972 Anti–Ballistic Missile Treaty

The United States of America and the Union of Soviet Socialist Republics, hereinafter referred to as the Parties,

Proceeding from the premise that nuclear war would have devastating consequences for all mankind,

Considering that effective measures to limit anti–ballistic missile systems would be a substantial factor in curbing the race in strategic offensive arms and would lead to a decrease in the risk of outbreak of war involving nuclear weapons,

Proceeding from the premise that the limitation of anti–ballistic missile systems, as well as certain agreed measures with respect to the limitation of strategic offensive arms, would contribute to the creation of more favorable conditions for further negotiations on limiting strategic arms,

Mindful of their obligations under Article VI of the Treaty on the Non-Proliferation of Nuclear Weapons,

Declaring their intention to achieve at the earliest possible date the cessation of the nuclear arms race and to take effective measures toward reductions in strategic arms, nuclear disarmament, and general and complete disarmament,

Desiring to contribute to the relaxation of international tension and the strengthening of trust between States,

Have agreed as follows:

Source: *Treaties and Other International Acts, Series 7503* (Washington, D.C.: U.S. Dept. of State, 1973).

ARTICLE I

1. Each Party undertakes to limit anti–ballistic missile (ABM) systems and to adopt other measures in accordance with the provisions of the Treaty.

2. Each Party undertakes not to deploy ABM systems for a defense of the territory of its country and not to provide a base for such a defense, and not to deploy ABM systems for defense of an individual region except as provided for in Article III of this Treaty.

ARTICLE II

1. For the purpose of this Treaty an ABM system is a system to counter strategic ballistic missiles or their elements in flight trajectory, currently consisting of:

(a) ABM interceptor missiles, which are interceptor missiles constructed and deployed for an ABM role, or of a type tested in an ABM mode;

(b) ABM launchers, which are launchers constructed and deployed for launching ABM interceptor missiles; and

(c) ABM radars, which are radars constructed and deployed for an ABM role, or of a type tested in an ABM mode.

2. The ABM system components listed in paragraph 1 of this Article include those which are:

(a) operational;

(b) under construction;

(c) undergoing testing;

(d) undergoing overhaul, repair or conversion; or

(e) mothballed.

ARTICLE III

Each Party undertakes not to deploy ABM systems or their components except that:

(a) within one ABM systems deployment area having a radius of one hundred and fifty kilometers and centered on the Party's national capital, a Party may deploy: (1) no more than one hundred ABM launchers and no more than one hundred ABM interceptor missiles at launch sites, and (2) ABM radars within no more than six ABM radar complexes, the area of each complex being circular and having a diameter of no more than three kilometers; and

(b) within one ABM system deployment area having a radius of one hundred and fifty kilometers and containing ICBM silo launchers, a Party may deploy: (1) no more than one hundred ABM radars and no more than one hundred ABM interceptors at launch sites, (2) two large phased-array ABM radars comparable in potential to corresponding ABM radars operational or under construction on the date of signature of the Treaty in an ABM system deployment area containing ICBM silo launchers, and (3) no more than eighteen ABM radars each having a potential less than the potential of the smaller of the above-mentioned two large phased-array radars.

ARTICLE IV

The limitations provided for in Article III shall not apply to ABM systems or their components used for development or testing, and located within current or additionally agreed test ranges. Each Party may have no more than a total of fifteen ABM launchers at test ranges.

ARTICLE V

1. Each Party undertakes not to develop, test, or deploy ABM systems or components which are sea-based, air-based, space-based, or mobile land-based.

2. Each Party undertakes not to develop, test, or deploy ABM launchers for launching more than one ABM interceptor missile at a time from each launcher, nor to modify deployed launchers to provide them with such a capability, nor to test, or deploy automatic or semi-automatic or other similar systems for rapid reload of ABM launchers.

ARTICLE VI

To enhance assurance of the effectiveness of the limitations on ABM systems and their components provided by this Treaty, each Party undertakes:

(a) not to give missiles, launchers, or radars, other than ABM interceptor missiles, ABM launchers, or ABM radars, capabilities to counter strategic ballistic missiles or their elements in flight trajectory, and not to test them in an ABM mode; and

(b) not to deploy in the future radars for early warning of strategic ballistic missile attack except at locations along the periphery of its national territory and oriented outward.

ARTICLE VII

Subject to the provisions of this treaty, modernization and replacement of ABM systems or their components may be carried out.

ARTICLE VIII

ABM systems or their components in excess of the numbers or outside the areas specified in the Treaty, as well as ABM systems or their components prohibited by this Treaty, shall be destroyed or dismantled under agreed procedures within the shortest possible agreed period of time.

ARTICLE IX

To assure the viability and effectiveness of the Treaty, each Party undertakes not to transfer to other States, and not to deploy outside national territory, ABM systems or their components limited by this Treaty.

ARTICLE X

Each Party undertakes not to assume any international obligation which would conflict with this Treaty.

ARTICLE XI

The Parties undertake to continue active negotiations for limitations on strategic offensive arms.

ARTICLE XII

1. For the purpose of providing assurance of compliance with the provisions of this Treaty, each Party shall use national technical means of verification at its disposal in a manner consistent with generally recognized principles of international law.

2. Each Party undertakes not to interfere with the national technical means of verification of the other Party operating in accordance with Paragraph 1 of the Article.

3. Each Party undertakes not to use deliberate concealment measures which impede verification by national technical means of compliance with the provisions of this Treaty. This obligation shall not require changes in current construction, assembly, conversion, or overhaul practices.

ARTICLE XIII

1. To promote the objectives and implementation of the provisions of this Treaty, the Parties shall establish promptly a Standing Consultative Commission, within the framework of which they will:

(a) consider questions concerning compliance with the obligations assumed and related situations which may be considered ambiguous;

(b) provide on a voluntary basis such information as either Party considers necessary to assure confidence in compliance with the obligations assumed;

(c) consider questions involving unintended interference with national technical means of verification;

(d) consider possible changes in the strategic situation which have a bearing on the provisions of the Treaty;

(e) agree upon procedures and dates for destruction or dismantling of ABM systems or their components in cases provided for by the provisions of this treaty;

(f) consider, as appropriate, possible proposals for further increasing the viability of this Treaty, including proposals for amendments in accordance with the provisions of the Treaty;

(g) consider, as appropriate, proposals for further measures aimed at limiting strategic arms.

2. The Parties through consultation shall establish and may amend as appropriate, Regulations for the Standing Consultative Commission governing procedures, composition and other relevant matters.

ARTICLE XIV

1. Each Party may propose amendments to this Treaty. Agreed amendments shall enter into force in accordance with the procedures governing the entry into force of this Treaty.

2. Five years after entry into force of this Treaty, and at five-year intervals thereafter, the Parties shall together conduct a review of the Treaty.

ARTICLE XV

1. This Treaty shall be of unlimited duration.

2. Each Party shall, in exercising its national sovereignty, have the right to withdraw from this Treaty if it decides that extraordinary event related to the subject matter of this Treaty have jeopardized its supreme interests. It shall give notice of its decision to the other Party prior to

withdrawal from the Treaty. Such notice shall include a statement of the extraordinary events the notifying Party regards as having jeopardized its supreme interests.

ARTICLE XVI

1. This Treaty shall be subject to ratification in accordance with the constitutional procedures of each Party. The Treaty shall enter into force on the day of the exchange of instruments of ratification.

2. This Treaty shall be registered pursuant to Article 102 of the Charter of the United Nations.

APPENDIX 17

Agreed Interpretations and Unilateral Statements Regarding the ABM Treaty

1. *Agreed Statements*

The document set forth below was agreed upon and initialed by the Heads of the Delegations on May 26, 1972:

[A]

The Parties understand that, in addition to the ABM radars which may be deployed in accordance with subparagraph (a) of Article III of the Treaty, those non-phased-array ABM radars operational on the date of signature of the Treaty within the ABM system deployment area for defense of the national capital may be retained.

[B]

The Parties understand that the potential (the product of mean emitted power in watts and antenna area in square meters) of the smaller of the two large phased-array ABM radars referred to in subparagraph (b) of Article III of the Treaty is considered for purposes of the Treaty to be three million.

[C]

The Parties understand that the center of the ABM system deployment area centered on the national capital and the center of the ABM

Source: *Treaties and Other International Acts, Series 7503* (Washington, D.C.: U.S. Dept. of State, 1973).

system deployment area containing ICBM silo launchers for each Party shall be separated by no less than thirteen hundred kilometers.

[D]

In order to ensure fulfillment of the obligation not to deploy ABM systems and their components except as provided in Article III of the Treaty, the Parties agree that in the event ABM systems based on other physical principles and including components capable of substituting for ABM interceptors missiles, ABM launchers, or ABM radars are created in the future, specific limitations on such systems and their components would be subject to discussion in accordance with Article XIII and agreement in accordance with Article XIV of the Treaty.

[E]

The Parties understand that Article V of the Treaty includes obligations not to develop, test, or deploy ABM interceptor missile for the delivery by each ABM interceptor missile of more than one independently guided warhead.

[F]

The Parties agree not to deploy phased-array radars having a potential (the product of mean emitted power in watts and antenna area in square meters) exceeding three million, except as provided for in Article III, IV and VI of the Treaty, or except for the purposes of tracking objects in outer space or for use as national technical means of verification.

[G]

The Parties understand that Article IX of the Treaty includes the obligation of the US and the USSR not to provide to other States technical descriptions or blue prints specially worked out for the construction of ABM systems and their components limited by the Treaty.

2. *Common Understandings*

Common understanding of the Parties on the following matter was reached during the negotiations:

A. Location of ICBM Defenses

The US Delegation made the following statement on May 26, 1972:

Article III of the ABM Treaty provides for each side on ABM system deployment area centered on its national capital and one ABM system deployment area containing ICBM silo launchers. The two sides have registered agreement on the following statement: "The Parties understand that the center of the ABM system deployment area centered on the national capital and the center of the ABM system deployment area containing ICBM silo launchers for each Party shall be separated by no less than thirteen hundred kilometers." In this connection, the US side notes that its ABM system deployment area for defense of ICBM silo launchers, located west of the Mississippi River, will be centered in the Grand Forks ICBM silo launcher deployment area. (See Initialed Statement [C].)

B. ABM Test Ranges
   The US Delegation made the following statement on April 26, 1972:

   Article IV of the ABM Treaty provides that "the limitations provided for in Article III shall not apply to ABM systems or their components used for development of testing, and located within current or additionally agreed test ranges." We believe it would be useful to assure that there is no misunderstanding as to current ABM test ranges. It is our understanding that ABM test ranges encompass the area within which ABM components are located for test purposes. The current US ABM test ranges are at White Sands, New Mexico, and at Kwajalein Atoll, and the current Soviet ABM test range is near Sary Shagan in Kazakhstan. We consider that non-phased array radars of types used for range safety or instrumentation purposes may be located outside of ABM test ranges. We interpret the reference in Article IV to "additionally agreed test ranges" to mean that ABM components will not be located at any other test ranges without prior agreement between our Governments that there will be such additional ABM test ranges.

   On May 5, 1972, the Soviet Delegation stated that there was a common understanding on what ABM test ranges were, that the use of the types of non-ABM radars for range safety or instrumentation was not limited under the Treaty, that the reference in Article IV to "additionally agreed" test ranges was sufficiently clear, and that national means permitted identifying current test ranges.

C. Mobile ABM Systems
   On January 28, 1972, the US Delegation made the following statement:

   Article V (I) of the Joint Draft Text of the ABM Treaty includes an undertaking not to develop, test, or deploy mobile land-based ABM systems and their components. On May 5, 1971, the US side indicated that, in its view, a prohibition on deployment of mobile ABM systems and their components would rule out the deployment of ABM launchers and radars which were not permanent fixed types. At that time, we asked for the Soviet view of this interpretation. Does the Soviet side agree with the US side's interpretation put forward on May 5, 1971?

On April 13, 1972, the Soviet Delegation said there is a general common understanding of this matter.

D. Standing Consultative Commission

Ambassador Smith made the following statement on May 22, 1972:

The United States proposes that the sides agree that, with regard to initial implementation of the ABM Treaty's Article XIII on the Standing Consultative Commission (SCC) and of the consultation Articles to the Accidents Agreement, agreement establishing the SCC will be worked out early in the follow-on SALT negotiations; until that is completed, the following arrangements will prevail: when SALT is in session, any consultation desired by either side under these Articles be carried out by the two SALT Delegations; when SALT is not in session, *ad hoc* arrangements for any desired consultations under these Articles may be made through diplomatic channels.

Minister Semenov replied that, on an *ad referendum* basis, he could agree that the US statement corresponded to the Soviet understanding.

E. Standstill

On May 6, 1972, Minister Semenov made the following statement:

In an effort to accommodate the wishes of the US side, the Soviet Delegation is prepared to proceed on the basis that the two sides will in fact observe the obligations of both the Interim Agreement and the ABM Treaty beginning from the date of signature of these two documents.

In reply, the US Delegation made the following statement on May 20, 1972:

The US agree in principle with the Soviet statement made on May 6 concerning observance of obligations beginning from date of signature but we would like to make clear our understanding that this means that, pending ratification and acceptance, neither side would take any action prohibited by the agreements after they had entered into force. This understanding would continue to apply in the absence of notification by either signatory of its intention not to proceed with ratification or approval.

The Soviet Delegation indicated agreement with the US statement.

3. *Unilateral Statements*
The following noteworthy unilateral statements were made during the negotiations by the United States Delegation:

A. Withdrawal from the ABM Treaty
On May 9, 1972, Ambassador Smith made the following statement:

The US Delegation has stressed the importance of the US Government attaches to achieving agreement on more complete limitations on strategic offensive arms, following agreement on an ABM Treaty and on an Interim Agreement on certain measure with respect to the limitations of strategic offensive arms. The US Delegation believes that an objective of the follow-on negotiations should be to constrain and reduce on a long-term basis threats to the survivability of our respective strategic retaliatory forces. The USSR Delegation has also indicated that the objectives of SALT would remain unfulfilled without the achievement of an agreement providing for more complete limitations on strategic offensive arms. Both sides recognize that the initial agreements would be steps toward the achievement of more complete limitations on strategic arms. If an agreement providing for more complete strategic offensive arms limitations were not achieved within five years, US supreme interest could be jeopardized. Should that occur, it would constitute a basis for withdrawal from the ABM Treaty. The US does not wish to see such a situation occur, nor do we believe that the USSR does. It is because we wish to prevent such a situation that we emphasize the importance that the US Government attaches to achievement of more complete limitations on strategic offensive arms. The US Executive will inform the Congress, in connection with Congressional consideration of the ABM Treaty and the Interim Agreement, of this statement of the US position.

B. Tested in ABM Mode
On April 7, 1972, the US Delegation made the following statement:

Article II of the Joint Text Draft uses the term "tested in an ABM mode," in defining ABM components, and Article VI includes certain obligations concerning such testing. We believe that the sides should have a common understanding of this phrase. First, we would note that the testing provisions of the ABM Treaty are intended to apply to testing which occurs after the date of signature of the Treaty, and not to any testing which may have occurred in the past. Next, we would amplify the remarks we have made on this subject during the previous Helsinki phase by setting forth the objectives which govern the US view on the subject, namely, while prohibiting testing of non-ABM components for ABM purposes: not to prevent testing of ABM components, and not to prevent testing of non-ABM components for non-ABM purposes. To clarify our interpretation of "tested in an ABM mode," we note that we would consider a launcher, missile or radar to be "tested in an ABM mode" if, for example, any of the following events occur: (1) a launcher is used to launch an ABM interceptor missile, (2) an interceptor missile is flight tested against a target vehicle which has a flight trajectory with characteristics of a strategic ballistic missile flight trajectory or an ABM interceptor missile or an ABM radar at the same test range, or is flight tested to an altitude inconsistent with interception of targets against which air defenses are deployed, (3) a radar makes measurements on a cooperative target vehicle of the kind referred to in item (2) above during the reentry portion of its trajectory or makes measurements in conjunction with the test of an ABM interceptor missile or an ABM radar at the same test range. Radars used for purposes such as range safety or instrumentation would be exempt from application of the criteria.

C. No-Transfer Article of ABM Treaty
On April 18, 1972, the US Delegation made the following statement:

In regard to this Article [IX], I have a brief and I believe self-explanatory statement to make. The US side wishes to make clear that the provisions of this Article do not set a precedent for whatever provision may be considered for a Treaty on Limiting Strategic Offensive Arms. The question of transfer of strategic offensive arms is a far more complex issue, which may require a different solution.

D. No Increase in Defense of Early Warning Radars
On July 28, 1970, the US Delegation made the following statement:

Since Hen House radars [Soviet ballistic-missile early-warning radars] can detect and track ballistic missile warheads at great distances, they have a significant ABM potential. Accordingly, the US would regard any increase in the defenses of such radars by surface-to-air missiles as inconsistent with an agreement.

The 1974 Protocol to the ABM Treaty

The United States of America and the Union of Soviet Socialist Republics, hereinafter referred to as the Parties,

Proceeding from the basic principles of relations between the United States of America and the Union of Soviet Socialist Republics signed on 29 May 1972,

Desiring to further the objectives of the Treaty between the United States of America and the Union of Soviet Socialist Republics on the Limitation of Anti–Ballistic Missile systems signed on 26 May 1972, hereinafter referred to as the Treaty,

Reaffirming their conviction that the adoption of further measures for the limitation of strategic arms would contribute to strengthening international peace and security,

Proceeding from the premise that further limitation of anti–ballistic missile systems will create more favorable conditions for the completion of work on a permanent agreement on more complete measures for the limitation of strategic offensive arms,

Have agreed as follows:

Article I

1. Each Party shall be limited at any one time to a single area out of the two provided in article III of the Treaty for deployment of anti–ballistic missile (ABM) systems or their components and accordingly shall not exercise its right to deploy an ABM system or its components in the second of the two ABM system deployment areas permitted by article III

Source: UN document A/9698, Annex III, 9 August 1974.

of the Treaty, except as an exchange of one permitted area for the other in accordance with article II of this Protocol.

2. Accordingly, except as permitted by article II of this Protocol: The United States of America shall not deploy an ABM system or its components in the area centered on its capital, as permitted by article III (a) of the Treaty, and the Soviet Union shall not deploy an ABM system or its components in the deployment area of intercontinental ballistic missile (ICBM) silo launchers as permitted by article III (b) of the Treaty.

Article II

1. Each Party shall have the right to dismantle or destroy its ABM system and the components thereof in the area where they are presently deployed and to deploy an ABM system or its components in the alternative area permitted by article III of the Treaty, provided that prior to initiation of construction, notification is given in accord with the procedure agreed to in the Standing Consultative Commission during the year beginning 3 October 1977 and ending 2 October 1978, or during any year which commences at five-year intervals thereafter, those being the years for periodic review of the Treaty, as provided in article XIV of the Treaty. This right may be exercised only once.

2. Accordingly, in the event of such notice, the United States would have the right to dismantle or destroy the ABM system and its components in the deployment area of ICBM silo launchers and to deploy an ABM system or its components in an area centered on its capital, as permitted by article III (a) of the Treaty, and the Soviet Union would have the right to dismantle or destroy the ABM system and its components in the area centered on its capital and to deploy an ABM system or its components in an area containing ICBM silo launchers, as permitted by article III (b) of the Treaty.

3. Dismantling or destruction and deployment of ABM systems or their components and the notification thereof shall be carried out in accordance with article VIII of the ABM Treaty and procedures agree to the Standing Consultative Commission.

Article III

The rights and obligations established by the Treaty remain in force and shall be complied with by the Parties except to the extent modified by the Protocol. In particular, the deployment of an ABM system or its components within the area selected shall remain limited by the levels and other requirements established by the Treaty.

Article IV

This Protocol shall be subject to ratification in accordance with the constitutional procedures of each Party. It shall enter into force on the day of the exchange of instruments of ratification and shall thereafter be considered an integral part of the Treaty.

The Biden Condition for Ratification of the INF Treaty

So it was: Resolved (two-thirds of the Senators present concurring therein), That the Senate advise and consent to ratification of the Treaty between the United States of America and the Union of Soviet Socialist Republics on the Elimination of Their Intermediate-Range and Shorter-Range Missiles, together with the Memorandum of Understanding and the two Protocols thereto, collectively referred to as the INF Treaty, all signed at the Washington summit on December 8, 1987 (Treaty Doc. 100-11), subject to the following:

Condition:

(1) Provided, that the Senate's advice and consent to ratification of the INF Treaty is subject to the condition, based on the Treaty Clauses of the Constitution, that—

(A) the United States shall interpret the Treaty in accordance with the common understanding of the Treaty shared by the President and the Senate at the time the Senate gave its advice and consent to ratification:

(B) such common understanding is based on:

(i) first, the text of the Treaty and the provisions of this resolution of ratification; and

(ii) second, the authoritative representation which were provided by the President and his representatives to the Senate and its Committees, in seeking Senate consent to ratification, insofar as such representations were directed to the meaning and legal effect of the text of the Treaty; and

---

Source: Arms Control Association, *Arms Control Today* 18 (September 1988).

(C) the United States shall not agree to or adopt an interpretation different from that common understanding except pursuant to Senate advice and consent to a subsequent treaty of protocol, or the enactment of a statute; and

(D) if, subsequent to ratification of the Treaty, a question arises as to the interpretation of a provision of the Treaty on which no common understanding was reached in accordance with paragraph (B), that provision shall be interpreted in accordance with applicable United States law.

APPENDIX **20**

The 1967 Treaty of Principles Governing the Activities of States in the Exploration and Use of Outer Space

The States Parties to this Treaty,

Inspired by the great prospects opening up before mankind as a result of man's entry into outer space,

Recognizing the common interest of all mankind in the progress of the exploration and use of outer space for peaceful purposes,

Believing that the exploration and use of outer space should be carried on for the benefit of all peoples irrespective of the degree of their economic or scientific development,

Desiring to contribute to broad international cooperation in the scientific as well as the legal aspects of the exploration and use of outer space for peaceful purposes,

Believing that such cooperation will contribute to the development of mutual understanding and to the strengthening of friendly relations between States and peoples,

Recalling resolution 1962 (XVIII), entitled "Declaration of Legal Principles Governing the Activities of States in the Exploration and Use of Outer Space," which was adopted unanimously by the United Nations General Assembly on 13 December 1963,

Recalling resolution 1884 (XVIII), calling upon States to refrain from placing in orbit around the earth any objects carrying nuclear weapons or

Source: *Treaty Series,* Vol. 610 (New York: United Nations).

any other kinds of weapons of mass destruction or from installing such weapons on celestial bodies, which was adopted unanimously by the United Nations General Assembly on 17 October 1963.

Taking account of United Nations General Assembly resolution 110 (II) of 3 November 1947, which condemned propaganda designed or likely to provoke or encourage any threat to the peace, breach of the peace or act of aggression, and considering that the aforementioned resolution is applicable to outer space.

Convinced that a Treaty on Principles Governing the Activities of States in the Exploration and Use of Outer Space, including the Moon and Other Celestial Bodies, will further the Purposes and Principles of the Charter of the United Nations.

Have agreed on the following:

Article I

The exploration and use of outer space, including the moon and other celestial bodies, shall be carried out for the benefit and in the interests of all countries, irrespective of their degree of economic or scientific development, and shall be the province of all mankind.

Outer space, including the moon and other celestial bodies, shall be free for exploration and use by all States without discrimination of any kind, on a basis of equality and in accordance with international law, and there shall be free access to all areas of celestial bodies.

There shall be freedom of scientific investigation if outer space, including the moon and other celestial bodies, and States shall facilitate and encourage international cooperation in such investigation.

Article II

Outer space, including the moon and other celestial bodies, is not subject to national appropriation by claim of sovereignty, by means of use of occupation, or by any other means.

Article III

States Parties to the Treaty shall carry on activities in the exploration and use of outer space, including the moon and other celestial bodies, in accordance with international law, including the Charter of the United Nations, in the interest of maintaining international peace and security and promoting international cooperation and understanding.

Article IV

States Parties to the Treaty undertake not to place in orbit around the earth any object carrying nuclear weapons or any other kinds of weapons of mass destruction, install such weapons of mass destruction, install such weapons on celestial bodies, or station such weapons in outer space in any other manner.

The moon and other celestial bodies shall be used by all States Parties to the Treaty establishment of military bases, installations and fortifications, the testing of any type weapons and the conduct of military maneuvering on celestial bodies shall be forbidden. The use of military personnel for scientific research or for any other peaceful purposes shall not be prohibited. The use of any equipment of the moon and other celestial bodies shall also not be prohibited.

Article V

States Parties to the Treaty shall regard astronauts as envoys of mankind in outer space and shall render to them all possible assistance in the event of accident, distress, or emergency landing on the territory of another State Party or on the high seas. When astronauts make such landing, they shall be safely and promptly returned to the State of registry of their space vehicles.

In carrying on activities in outer space and on celestial bodies, the astronauts of one State Party shall render all possible assistance to the astronauts of other States Parties.

States Parties to the Treaty shall immediately inform the other States Parties to the Treaty or the Secretary-General of the United Nations of any phenomena they discover in outer space, including the moon and other celestial bodies which could constitute a danger to the life or health of astronauts.

Article VI

States Parties to the Treaty shall bear international responsibility for national activities in outer space, including the moon and other celestial bodies, whether such activities are carried on by governmental agencies or by non-governmental entities, and for assuring that national activities are carried out in conformity with the provisions set forth in the present Treaty. The activities of non-governmental entities in outer space, including the moon and other celestial bodies, shall require authorization and continuing supervision by the appropriate State party to the Treaty. When activities are carried on in outer space, including the moon and other celestial bodies, by an international organization, responsibility for compliance with this Treaty shall be borne both by the international organization and by the States Parties to the Treaty participating in such organization.

Article VII

Each State Party to the Treaty that launches or procures the launching of an object into outer space, including the moon and other celestial bodies, and each State Party from whose territory or facility an object is launched, is internationally liable for damage to another State Party to the Treaty or to its natural or juridical persons by such object or its component parts on the Earth, in the air space or in outer space, including the moon and other celestial bodies.

Article VIII

A State Party to the Treaty on whose registry an object launched into outer space is carried shall retain jurisdiction and control over such object, and over any personnel thereof, while in outer space or on a celestial body. Ownership of objects launched into outer space, including objects landed or constructed on a celestial body, and of their component parts, is not affected by their presence in outer space or on a celestial body or by their return to the Earth. Such objects or component parts found beyond the limits of the State Party to the Treaty on whose registry they are carried shall be returned to that State Party, which shall, upon request, furnish identifying data prior to their return.

Article IX

In the exploration and use of outer space, including the moon and other celestial bodies, States Parties to the Treaty shall be guided by the principle of cooperation and mutual assistance and shall conduct all their activities in outer space, including the moon and other celestial bodies, with due regard to the corresponding interests of all other States Parties to the Treaty. States Parties to the Treaty shall pursue studies of outer space, including the moon and other celestial bodies, and conduct exploration of them so as to avoid their harmful contamination and also adverse changes in the environment of the Earth resulting from the introduction of extraterrestrial matter and, where necessary, shall adopt appropriate measures for this purpose. If a State Party to the Treaty has reason to believe that an activity or experiment planned by it or its nationals in outer space, including the moon and other celestial bodies, would cause potentially harmful interference with activities of other States Parties in the peaceful exploration and use of outer space, including the moon and other celestial bodies, it shall undertake appropriate international consultations before proceeding with any such activity or experiment. A State Party to the Treaty which has reason to believe that an activity or experiment planned by another State Party in outer space, including the moon and other celestial bodies, would cause potentially harmful exploration and use of outer space, including exploration and use of outer space, including the moon and other celestial bodies, may request consultation concerning the activity or experiment.

Article X

In order to promote international cooperation in the exploration and use of outer space, including the moon and other celestial bodies, conformity with the purposes of this Treaty, the States Parties to the Treaty shall consider on a basis of equality any requests by other States Parties to the Treaty to be afforded an opportunity to observe the flight of space objects launched by the States.

The nature of such an opportunity for observation and the conditions under which it could be afforded shall be determined by agreement between the States concerned.

Article XI

In order to promote international cooperation in the peaceful exploration and use of outer space, States Parties to the Treaty conducting activities in outer space, including the moon and other celestial bodies, agree to inform the Secretary-General of the United Nations as well as the public and the international scientific community, to the greatest extent feasible and practicable, of the nature, conduct, locations and results of such activities. On receiving the said information, the Secretary-General of the United Nations should be prepared to disseminate it immediately and effectively.

Article XII

All stations, installations, equipment and space vehicles on the moon and other celestial bodies shall be open to representatives of other States Parties to the Treaty on a basis of reciprocity. Such representatives shall give reasonable advance notice of a projected visit, in order that appropriate consultations may be taken to assure safety and to avoid interference with normal operations in the facility to be visited.

Article XIII

The provisions of this Treaty shall apply to the activities of State Parties to the Treaty in the exploration and use of outer space, including the moon and other celestial bodies, whether such activities are carried on by a single State Party to the Treaty or jointly with other States, including cases where they are carried on within the framework of international inter-governmental organizations.

Any practical questions arising in connection with activities carried on by international inter-governmental organizations in the exploration and use of outer space, including the moon and other celestial bodies, shall be resolved by the States Parties to the Treaty either with the appropriate international organization or with one or more States members of that international organization, which are Parties to this Treaty.

Article XIV

1. This Treaty shall be open to all States for signature. Any State which does not sign this Treaty before its entry into force in accordance with paragraph 3 of this Article may accede to it at any time.

2. This Treaty shall be subject to ratification by signatory States. Instruments of ratification and instruments of accession shall be deposited with the Governments of the United Kingdom of Great Britain and Northern Ireland, the Union of Soviet Socialist Republics and the United States of America, which are hereby designated the Depository Governments.

3. This Treaty shall enter into force upon the deposit of instruments of ratification by five Governments including the Governments designated as Depository governments under this Treaty.

4. For States whose instruments of ratification or accession are deposited subsequent to the entry into force of this Treaty, it shall enter into force on the date of the deposit of their instruments of ratification or accession.

5. The Depository Governments shall promptly inform all signatory and acceding States of the date of each signature, the date of deposit of each instrument of ratification of and accession to this Treaty, the date of its entry into force and other notices.

6. This Treaty shall be registered by the Depository Governments pursuant to Article 102 of the Charter of the United Nations.

Article XV

Any State Party to the Treaty may propose amendments to the Treaty. Amendments shall enter into force for each State Party to the Treaty accepting the amendments up their acceptance by a majority of the States Parties to the Treaty and thereafter for each remaining State Party to the Treaty on the date of acceptance by it.

Article XVI

Any State Party to the Treaty may give notice of its withdrawal from the Treaty one year after its entry into force by written notification to the Depository Governments. Such withdrawal shall take effect one year from the date of receipt of this notification.

Article XVII

This Treaty, of which the English, Russian, French, Spanish and Chinese texts are equally authentic, shall be deposited in the archives of the Depository Governments. Duly certified copies of this Treaty shall be transmitted by the Depository Governments to the Governments of the signatory and acceding States.

The 1963 Partial Test Ban Treaty

The Governments of the United States of America, the United Kingdom of Great Britain and Northern Ireland, and the Union of Soviet Socialist Republics, hereinafter referred to as the "Original Parties,"

Proclaiming as their principal aim the speediest possible achievement of an agreement on general and complete disarmament under strict international control in accordance with the objectives of the United Nations which would put an end to the armaments race and eliminate the incentive to the production and testing of all kinds of weapons, including nuclear weapons,

Seeking to achieve the discontinuance of all test explosions of nuclear weapons for all time, determined to continue negotiations to this end, and desiring to put an end to the contamination of man's environment by radioactive substances,

Have agreed as follows:

Article I

1. Each of the parties to the Treaty undertakes to prohibit, to prevent, and not to carry out any nuclear weapon test explosion, or any other nuclear explosion, at any place under its jurisdiction or control:

(a) in the atmosphere; beyond its limits, including outer space, or under water, including territorial waters or high seas; or

(b) in any other environment if such explosion causes radioactive debris to be present outside the territorial limits of the State under whose

Source: *Treaty Series,* Vol. 480 (New York: United Nations).

jurisdiction or control such explosion is conducted. It is understood in this connection that the provisions of this subparagraph are without prejudice to the conclusion of a treaty resulting in the permanent banning of all nuclear test explosions, including all such explosions underground, the conclusion of which, as the Parties have stated in the Preamble to the Treaty, they seek to achieve.

2. Each of the parties to this Treaty undertakes furthermore to refrain from causing, encouraging, or in any way participating in, the carrying out of any nuclear weapon test explosion, or any other nuclear explosion, anywhere which would take place in any of the environments described, or have the effect referred to, in paragraph 1 of this Article.

Article II

1. Any Party may propose amendments to this Treaty. The text of any proposed amendment shall be submitted to the Depository Governments which shall circulate it to all Parties to this Treaty. There after, if requested the Depository Governments shall convene a conference, to which they shall invite all the Parties, to consider such amendment.

2. Any amendment to this Treaty must be approved by a majority of the votes of all the Original Parties. The amendment shall enter into force for all Parties upon the deposit of instruments of ratification by a majority of all the Parties, including the instruments of ratification of all of the Original Parties.

Article III

1. This Treaty shall be open to all States for signature. Any State which does not sign this Treaty before its entry into force in accordance with paragraph 3 of this Article may accede to it at any time.

2. This Treaty shall be subject to ratification by signatory States. Instruments of ratification and instruments of accession shall be deposited with the Governments of the Original Parties—the United States of America, the United Kingdom of Great Britain and Northern Ireland, and the Union of Soviet Socialist Republics—which are hereby designated the Depository Governments.

3. This Treaty shall enter into force after its ratification by all the Original Parties and the deposit of their instruments of ratification.

4. For States whose instruments of ratification or accession are deposited subsequent to the entry into force of this Treaty, it shall enter into force on the date of the deposit of their instruments of ratification or accession.

5. The Depository Governments shall promptly inform all signatory and acceding States of the data of each signature, the date of deposit of

each instrument of ratification of and accession to this Treaty, the date of its entry into force, and the date of the deposit of their instruments of ratification or accession.

6. This Treaty shall be registered by the Depository Governments pursuant to Article 102 of the Charter of the United Nations.

Article IV

This treaty shall be of unlimited duration.

Each Party shall in exercising its national sovereignty have the right to withdraw from the Treaty if it decides that extraordinary events, related to the subject matter of this Treaty, have jeopardized the supreme interests of its country. It shall give notice of such withdrawal to all other Parties to the Treaty three months in advance.

Article V

This Treaty, of which the English and Russians tests are equally authentic, shall be deposited in the archives of the Depository Governments. Duly certified copies of this Treaty shall be transmitted by the Depository Governments to the Governments of the signatory and acceding States.

APPENDIX 22

The 1974 Agreement for the Prevention of Nuclear War

The United States of America and the Union of Soviet Socialist Republics, hereinafter referred to as the Parties,

Guided by the objectives of strengthening world peace and international security,

Conscious that nuclear war would have devastating consequences for mankind,

Proceeding from the desire to bring about conditions in which the danger of an outbreak of nuclear war anywhere in the world would be reduced and ultimately eliminated,

Proceeding from their obligations under the Charter of the United Nations regarding the maintenance of peace, refraining from the threat or use of force, and the avoidance of war, and in conformity with the agreements to which either Party has subscribed,

Proceeding from the Basic Principles of Relations between the United States of America and the Union of Soviet Socialist Republics signed in Moscow on May 20, 1972,

Reaffirming that the development of relations between the United States of America and the Union of Soviet Socialist Republics is not directed against other countries and their interests,

Have agreed as follows:

Article I

The United States and the Soviet Union agree that an objective of

Source: *Treaties and Other International Acts, Series 7654* (Washington, D.C.: U.S. Dept. of State, 1973).

their policies is to remove the danger of nuclear war and of the use of nuclear weapons.

Accordingly, the Parties agree that they will act in such a manner as to prevent the development of situations capable of causing a dangerous exacerbation of their relations, as to avoid military confrontations, and as to exclude the outbreak of nuclear war between them and between either of the Parties and other countries.

Article II

The Parties agree, in accordance with Article I and to realize the objective stated in that Article, to proceed from the premise that each Party will refrain from the threat or use of force against the other Party and against other countries, in circumstances which may endanger international peace and security. The Parties agree that they will be guided by these considerations in the formulation of their foreign policies and in their actions in the field of international relations.

Article III

The Parties undertake to develop their relations with each other and with other countries in a way consistent with the purposes of the Agreement.

Article IV

If at any time relations between the Parties or between either party and other countries appear to involve the risk of a nuclear conflict, or if relations between countries not parties to this Agreement appear to involve the risk of nuclear war between the United States of America and the Union of Soviet Socialist Republics or between either Party and other countries, the United States and the Soviet Union, acting in accordance with the provisions of this Agreement, shall immediately enter into urgent consultations with each other and make every effort to avert this risk.

Article V

Each Party shall be free to inform the Security Council of the United Nations, the Secretary General to the United Nations and the Governments of allied or other countries of the progress and outcome of consultations initiated in accordance with Article IV of this agreement.

Article VI

Nothing in this Agreement shall affect or impair:

(a) the inherent right of individual or collective self-defense as envisaged by Article 51 of the Charter of the United Nations,

(b) the provisions of the Charter of the United Nations, including those relating to the maintenance or restoration of international peace and security, and

(c) the obligations undertaken by either Party toward its allies or other countries in treaties, agreements, and other appropriate documents.

Article VII

This agreement shall be of unlimited duration.

Article VIII

This Agreement shall enter into force upon signature.

APPENDIX 23

Brilliant Pebble Boost-Phase Defense Requirements

The decision to replace the originally planned Space-Based Interceptor (SBI) for the boost-phase layer of a Phase I defense with Brilliant Pebbles was made because of several problems with the earlier version of SBI. The cost of Phase I deployment appeared to decrease with the introduction of Brilliant Pebbles, and the novelty of the concept was seen as more likely to gain political support. However, calculations of the capabilities and requirements of this defense reveal its limitations. Questions on the cost effectiveness of the Brilliant Pebbles defense and its capabilities will be examined.

A recent paper by Canavan and Teller addressed the defense capabilities for quite idealistic circumstances: defense against Soviet SS-18s over the boost-phase time of about 300 seconds and post-boost-phase time of another 300 seconds.[1] The ICBMs were taken to be spread over an area of radius 1800 kilometers, and the interceptors to be in an optimum orbit to cover the Soviet missile fields. This provided about a 20% accessibility of the defense to the missiles. Furthermore, it was noted that 20–40% of the warheads (2–4 warheads of the 10 warheads per missile) would be deployed before the booster or bus could be taken out by the Brilliant Pebbles defense.

By estimating a total cost (procurement, operating, deployment, and silo-basing) of $200 million for each ICBM and $6 million for each Brilliant Pebble interceptor, then the requirement of 5 interceptors in orbit for 1 accessible to the ICBM fields led to a claim of a 7:1 cost advantage to the defense. Another assumption in this claim is that the interceptors can take out 100% of the missiles they are fired at.

However, this calculation is misleading because the defense capabilities would be much more limited than for the assumed model, as pointed out by Garwin.[2] The cost effectiveness would be much lower with Soviet SS-25s (already deployed) or similar missiles deployed in a much smaller area (100 kilometers radius or less). A response to the deployment of a space defense would likely be an expansion of the deployment of these missiles. Calculations will be made with that model to determine the availability of the defense to the missiles and the number of Brilliant Pebble interceptors required. The cost effectiveness of a robust boost-phase defense is addressed first, and consideration on the boost and post-boost-phase counters with the more limited defense planned by SDIO considered later. In the post-boost phase there is rapid leakage from warheads deployed before effective countering of all the buses can occur.

The distance over which a Brilliant Pebble interceptor can access an ICBM in the boost-phase has limits very similar to the homing rocket limits discussed in Chapter 6 and Appendix 13. The principal new aspects of a Brilliant Pebbles defense is that the interceptors are smaller and have a greater number of independent vehicles for an area of defense. One can calculate the area that each Brilliant Pebble interceptor could cover from the range available for the velocities that can be attained, and derive the minimum number required for a boost-phase defense against a constellation of missiles launched.

Denote the boost-phase time by t_b and the time of delay from the launch of the missiles to the detection of the launch, preparation, and firing of the Pebbles by the defense as t_o. Denote the average velocity of the Brilliant Pebble interceptor as v_m. Then the maximum range of each Brilliant Pebble for a boost-phase defense is $r = v_m(t_b - t_o)$. The area that it can cover in the phase defense is then πr^2. For the Brilliant Pebble defense in low Earth orbit, only a fraction of the Brilliant Pebbles are in a region that can access the Soviet missiles.

If the missiles are concentrated in a small area (which they will be if Brilliant Pebbles is deployed) and the Brilliant Pebble interceptors are placed in the orbit for optimum coverage of the Soviet ICBMs (at an inclination with respect to the equator at a similar angular range as the latitudinal range of the missile fields) the fraction B of interceptors available to counter the missiles is given by:

$$B = \pi y r^2 / 4\pi R^2 = y[v_m(t_b - t_o)]^2 / 4R^2 \tag{1}$$

where R is the radius of the Earth (6377 km), y is the concentration factor of interceptors within range of the missiles from an optimization of the orbital inclinations (the advantage factor over a uniform satellite coverage, taken as 3 for the chemical laser defense in Chapter 3 and Appendix

5, and denoted by z in Teller and Canavan), and the denominator is just the area of the Earth's surface.

Knowing the availability of B of the Brilliant Pebbles to the missiles, then the number of Brilliant Pebbles required to defend against the missiles is:

$$N = M/\epsilon_{acc}B = 4MR^2/\epsilon_{acc}y[v_m(t_b - t_o)]^2 \tag{2}$$

where ϵ_{acc} is the probability of an interceptor successfully countering a missile within range.

The orbital concentration factor y as a function of the launch inclination angle for $a \gg 1$ is given by:[3]

$$y = 2a^{1/4}/\pi[\sin(2I)]^{1/2} \tag{3}$$

where a is the absentee ratio for a uniform satellite coverage:

$$a \approx 4\pi R^2/\pi r^2 = 4R^2/[v_m(t_b - t_o)]^2 \tag{4}$$

The central launch latitude for Soviet ICBM fields is about 55°, so taking that value for I, $\sin 2I = 0.940$.

As an example, suppose the accuracy ϵ_{acc} in destroying a missile for each Brilliant Pebble to be 90% (very optimistic with the use of appropriate countermeasure), the boost-phase time to be 180 seconds (as on current Soviet SS-25s), the number of missiles to be taken out as $M = 1,000$ (a deployment of 1,000 warheads on single-warhead SS-25 boosters as a countertactic), and the time of warning and release to be 30 seconds. Lt. Gen. George Monahan testified before the Senate Appropriations Committee in early 1990 that this would be 50–100 seconds, so the 30-second assumption is very minimal. The maximum velocity that the interceptors can achieve is about 10 kilometers/second with a total Pebble weight of 100 pounds, as discussed for homing rockets in Chapter 6, so the average velocity v_m will be taken as an optimistic 6 kilometers/second. Then $y = 2.47$, so the availability is $B = 1.23\%$ and the minimum number of Brilliant Pebble interceptors required is 81,000.

Table A23.1 contains a listing of the number of interceptors required for an effective boost-phase defense (assuming there are no special countermeasures) for different values of the boost-phase time t_b. The table shows that over 100,000 interceptors will be required for a defense against 1,000 boosters with boost-phase time the same as many U.S. ICBMs.

Using the total cost estimate (development, production, deployment, and maintenance of the defense after deployment) of each Brilliant Pebble

Table A23.1. Number of Brilliant Pebble interceptors required for 1,000 missile boosters

t_b (sec)	y	B	N
180	2.47	1.23%	81,235
150	2.76	0.88%	113,533
120	3.19	0.57%	174,780
90	3.91	0.31%[a]	321,092
50	. . .	0.00%	inaccessible

Note: The value of t_o, the time necessary for warning and targeting before countering the missile, is taken as 30 seconds (an optimistic value); y = increased factor in absentee ratio by optimizing the orbits.

[a] This may be much smaller than estimated by the equation because the missiles are getting out of boost-phase time range of the closest interceptors.

in Canavan and Teller at $6 million (the direct cost is $1 million), then the cost of the 100,000 minimum needed for defense against 1,000 ICBMs is around $600 billion. For a total cost estimate of ICBMs at $200 million (the direct cost of SS-25s is about $30 million), the cost of 1,000 ICBMs will be around $200 billion. The (defense/offense) cost ratio is equal to 3. Thus the defense is not cost effective, and this more realistic (defense/offense) cost-ratio estimate for a basing of SS-25s is about a factor of 20 larger than the quoted estimate for an idealistic defense against Soviet SS-18s.

The (defense/offense) ratio goes up as the boost-phase time shortens. If fast-burn boosters are added, the direct cost of each ICBM increases to $60 million, but the interceptors cannot access the missiles in the boost phase, no matter how large the number. The (defense/offense) cost ratio goes to infinity.

The initial purpose of the Brilliant Pebbles defense set forth by the proposers and later by SDIO, however, is not to have a highly effective defense, but only a partial defense (the claimed 10–30% boost-phase kill). There are several reasons for this:

1. The serious difficulties in using a Brilliant Pebbles defense to effectively counter most of the boosters in a major attack, such as the ones outlined above.

2. The intention only to use Brilliant Pebbles in the first-phase defense. Spending several hundred billion dollars for the initial phase that will be replaced with laser and particle-beam defense on later phases is ludicrous.

3. The intention to use the Brilliant Pebbles only to protect the ICBM silos and military installations against a preemptive first strike. There is a big assumption here that a preemptive first strike could be

effective, which is not supported by the facts.

4. The implicit effort to toe the line so that the Soviets will not be motivated to make a major expansion of their new missiles, or deploy fast-burn boosters and a variety of countermeasures.

Consistent with these goals the proposed Phase I defense is to use 4,000 Brilliant Pebble interceptors. It is easily determined from Equation (2) how many missiles the 4,000 Brilliant Pebble interceptors can take out for given missile boost-phase times. In this case $N = 4,000$ and M is to be determined. As before, v_m is taken as 6 kilometers/second, ϵ_{acc} as 90% (an optimistic value), and the warning and preparation time t_o as the minimal 30 seconds.

The number of ICBMs that can be countered, for interceptors in optimum orbits for covering the Soviet ICBM fields, is shown in Table A23.2. Shown separately are M_{cb}, the number of missiles countered in the boost phase, and M_{cp}, the number of buses countered in the post-boost phase. The post-boost-phase time is assumed to be 40 seconds for all cases (this time could possibly be reduced to as short as 10 seconds with current technology by deployment in clusters). For post-boost-phase counters, there is a considerable warhead leakage from warheads already deployed before the bus is countered — over 50% of the warheads in the countered buses.

Table A23.2 contains results for current and future boosters under the assumption that no countermeasures are present that foil the defense. The defense will be able to counter 44 missiles at the current SS-25 boost-phase time, and capabilities rapidly decrease as the time available to counter in the boost phase decreases. With fast-burn boosters, effectively no countering is possible in either the boost or post-boost phases.

The proclaimed purposes of strategic defense, which were revised in 1990 because of the ending of the cold war, are to avoid an accidental

Table A23.2. Number of ICBMs countered by 4,000 Brilliant Pebble interceptors

t_b (sec)	M_{cb}	M_{cp}[a]	Boost-Time Examples
180	44	19	Current Soviet SS-25
150	32	17	Upgraded U.S. MX
120	21	15	
90	11[b]	13	Current U.S. Pershing II
50	0	0	Fast-burn boosters

Note: M_{cb} = boosters (missiles) countered in boost phase; M_{cp} = buses countered in the post-boost phase.

[a]In post-boost-phase counters over 50% of the warheads will already be deployed before countering.

[b]This may be much smaller than estimated by the equation because the missiles are getting out of boost-phase time range of the closest interceptors.

nuclear launch and to protect against other countries that may develop long-range ballistic missiles and a nuclear capability in the future. For a defense against accidental nuclear launch as well as other countries with a future possibility nuclear weapons and long-range ballistic missiles, a nearly uniform global network of Brilliant Pebble interceptors will be necessary rather than one concentrated on Soviet ICBM fields. The reason for this necessity includes the arbitrary location of SLBMs at sea as well as the widespread distribution of countries with possible nuclear and ballistic missile capabilities. Thus the factor $y = 1$ in Equations (1)–(3) and the number of missiles that 4,000 Brilliant Pebbles can take out correspondingly decreases.

The shorter flight path (since shorter distances are traveled) and variable launch location of SLBMs will decrease the ability to counter SLBMs. Thus the capability required for an SLBM + ICBM defense can increase by a factor greater than y over that required for an ICBM-only defense.

Table A23.3 contains the number of missiles that can be countered by Brilliant Pebbles in the boost and post-boost phases for current SLBM boost-phase times and for shorter times easily available with fast-burn boosters. The efficiency ϵ_{acc} is likely to be much lower for SLBMs than for ICBMs, but the 90% value is also used in this table.

Table A23.3. Number of missiles countered by a global defense of 4,000 interceptors

t_b (sec)	M_{cb}	M_{cp}[a]	Boost-Time Examples
180	18	11	Current U.S. Trident II
120	6	7	Current U.S. Poseidon
90	3[b]	5	
50	0	0	Fast-burn boosters

[a]In post-boost-phase counters over 50% of the warheads will already be deployed before countering.

[b]This may be effectively 0 because the missiles are getting out of boost-phase time range of the closest interceptors.

It appears that the defense will be able to protect the launch of a small number of long-range missiles launched accidentally if they do not contain effective countermeasures against Brilliant Pebbles. However, the system provides a significantly lower (about one-third) protection against an accidental launch of shorter-range SLBMs. It cannot provide protection against fast-burn boosters. Furthermore, it will give us no protection against an accidental cruise-missile launch or any nuclear attack in any form not using ballistic missiles. With the $55 billion direct-cost estimate for this Phase I defense (a very conservative estimate) and the indirect costs for development, deployment, and maintenance, the total costs for this first-phase defense will easily be $200 billion–$300 billion. Rather than pursuing this very expensive and very limited approach to prevention, it is undoubtedly wiser to explore other less expensive ways of preventing accidental nuclear war.

Notes

1. Military Uses of Space

1. "Particle Beams as ABM Weapons: General and Physicists Differ," *Science* 196 (April 22, 1977): 407–8; "The Great Russian 'Death-Beam' Flap," *Science News* 111 (May 21, 1977): 329–30.

2. "Weapons Bureaucracy Spurns Star Wars Goal," *Science* 224 (April 6, 1984): 32–33.

3. U.S. Congress, Office of Technology Assessment, *Ballistic Missile Defense Technologies,* OTA-ISC-254 (Washington, D.C.: U.S. Government Printing Office, September 1985).

4. "SDI Policy Linked to Protection of People," *Aviation Week and Space Technology* 122 (April 29, 1985): 225–26.

5. *New York Times,* September 6, 1986, p. A9.

6. Alexander Flax, "Ballistic Missile Defense: Concepts and History," *Daedalus: Weapons in Space, Vol. I* 114 (Spring 1985): 33–52.

7. David Schwartz, "Past and Present: The Historical Legacy," in Ashton Carter and David Schwartz (eds.), *Ballistic Missile Defense* (Washington, D.C.: Brookings Institution, 1984); Richard Garwin, Kurt Gottfried, and Henry Kendall, *The Fallacy of Star Wars* (New York: Vintage, 1984), chap. 1.

8. Phillip Boffey, William Broad, Leslie Gelb, Charles Mohr, and Holcomb Noble, *Claiming the Heavens* (New York: Times Books, 1988), chaps. 1–2; Greg Herkin, "The Earthly Origins of Star Wars," *Bulletin of the Atomic Scientists* 43 (October 1987): 20–28.

9. "Red Flag at a Weapons Lab," *Time,* January 18, 1988, p. 52; Deborah Blum, "Weird Science: Livermore's X-Ray Laser Flap," *Bulletin of the Atomic Scientists* 44 (July-August 1988): 7–13.

10. "Militarizing the Last Frontier: The Space Weapons Race," *Defense Monitor* 12, no. 5 (1983).

11. See note 3, above.

3. Boost-Phase Intercept Systems

1. Kosta Tsipis, "Laser Weapons," *Scientific American* 245 (1981): 51–56.

2. *Physics Today* 40 (May 1987): S1–S16.

3. B. M. Blechman and V. A. Utgoff, *Fiscal and Economic Implications of Strategic Defenses* (Baltimore: School of Advanced International Studies at Johns Hopkins, Westview/Foreign Policy Institute, 1986), no. 12.

4. Hans Bethe, Richard Garwin, Kurt Gottfried, and Henry Kendall, "Space-Based Ballistic Missile Defense," *Scientific American* 251 (October 1984): 39–49.

5. See note 2.

6. See note 4.

7. See note 2.

8. John Parmentola and Kosta Tsipis, "Particle Beam Weapons," *Scientific American* 240 (1979): 54–65.

9. "Sandia Laser Experiment May Aid Beam Weapon Development," *Aviation Week and Space Technology* 122 (April 22, 1985): 26.

10. David Hobbes, *Space Warfare* (Englewood Cliffs, N.J.: Prentice-Hall, 1986) section on Kinetic Energy Weapons.

11. Craig Covault, "SDI Delta Space Experiment to Aid Kill-Vehicle Design," *Aviation Week and Space Technology* 125 (September 15, 1986): 18–19.

4. Midcourse and Terminal Interception

1. G. Letteer, "A Study of Interactive Discrimination in the Midcourse Phase," *Physics and Society* (American Physical Society) 17 (October 1988): 8–9.

2. "Midcourse ABM Defense Recommended," *Aviation Week and Space Technology* 121 (October 29, 1984): 23–34.

3. Bruce Smith, "Boeing Prepares AOA Sensor for Flight Test on 767," *Aviation Week and Space Technology* 129 (November 7, 1988): 40–41.

4. Samuel Glasstone and Philip Dolan, *The Effects of Nuclear Weapons* (U.S. Department of Defense, Energy Research and Development Administration, 1977), chap. 10; Richard Garwin and Hans Bethe, "Anti–Ballistic Missile Systems," *Scientific American* 219 (March 1968): 21–31.

5. Samuel Glasstone and Philip Dolan, *The Effects of Nuclear Weapons* (U.S. Department of Defense, Energy Research and Development Administration, 1977), chap. 11.

5. Requirements for a Defensive System

1. James Bruce, Bruce MacDonald, and Ronald Tammen, *Star Wars at the Crossroads: The Strategic Defense Initiative after Five Years,* staff report to Senators Bennett Johnston, Dale Bumpers, and William Proxmire (June 1988).

2. National Research Council, *Advanced Power Sources for Space Missions* (Washington, D.C.: National Academy Press, 1989).

3. Colin Norman, "Space Reactors and Arms Control," *Science* 243 (January 27, 1989): 474.

4. Robert Zirkle, "A Tangled Network: Command and Control for SDI," in John Tirman (ed.), *Empty Promise: The Growing Case Against Star Wars* (Boston: Beacon Press, 1986).

5. Greg Nelson and David Redell, "Could We Trust the SDI Software," in John Tirman (ed.), *Empty Promise: The Growing Case Against Star Wars* (Boston: Beacon Press, 1986).

6. Herbert Lin, "The Development of Software for Ballistic Missile Defense," *Scientific American* 253 (December 1985): 46–53.

7. Solicitation of research proposals from universities by the Strategic Defense Initiative Organization, 1985.

8. David Parnas, "Software Aspects of Strategic Defense Systems," *American Scientist* 73, no. 5 (September-October 1985): 432–40.

6. Countermeasures

1. Richard Garwin and Hans Bethe, "Anti–Ballistic Missile Systems," *Scientific American* 219 (March 1968): 21–31.

2. Richard Garwin, "The Soviet Response: New Missiles and Countermeasures," in John Tirman (ed.), *Empty Promise: The Growing Case Against Star Wars* (Boston: Beacon Press, 1986).

3. Robert Jastrow, "The War Against Star Wars," *Commentary* 78 (December 1984): 19–25.

4. Frank von Hippel, "Attacks on Star Wars Critics a Diversion," *Bulletin of the Atomic Scientists* 41 (April 1985): 8–10.

7. Phased Deployment of a Strategic Defense

1. Colin Norman, "Debate Over SDI Enters New Phase," *Science* 235 (January 16, 1987): 277–80; John Cushman, Jr., "Weinberger Outlines Strategy on Missile Shield," *New York Times,* January 13, 1987, A1.

2. Douglas Waller and James Bruce, *SDI: Progress and Challenges, Part II,* staff report submitted to Senators William Proxmire and Bennett Johnston (March 1987).

3. See note 2.

4. James Bruce, Bruce MacDonald, and Ronald Tammen, *Star Wars at the Crossroads: The Strategic Defense Initiative After Five Years,* staff report submitted to Senators Bennett Johnston, Dale Bumpers, and William Proxmire (March 1988); *SDI: Technology, Survivability, and Software* (Washington, D.C.: Office of Technology Assessment, 1988); Wayne Biddle, "Star Wars: The Dream Diminished," *Discover* 8 (July 1987): 26–38.

5. J. Garner, E. Gerry, Robert Jastrow, W. Nierenberg, and F. Seitz, *Deployment of Missile Defenses in the 1990's,* Marshall Institute Report (December 1986).

6. See note 2.

7. Christopher Cunningham, Tom Morgan, and Patrick Duffy, *Near Term Ballistic Missile Defense,* Lawrence Livermore Laboratory Report (1987).

8. B. M. Blechman and V. A. Utgoff, *Fiscal and Economic Implications of Strategic Defenses* (Baltimore: School of Advanced International Studies at Johns Hopkins, Westview/Foreign Policy Institute, 1986).

9. See Bruce et al., note 4.

10. See *SDI: Technology,* note 4.

11. "On the Road to a More Stable Peace," address by Paul Nitze on February 20, 1985, *Department of State Bulletin* 85 (April 1985): 27–29; see Bruce et al., note 4.

12. *1985 Congressional Quarterly Almanac XLI* (Washington, D.C.: Congress, 1986): 130–38.

13. B. Morel, "SDI Near-Term Deployment II. Too Early," *Physics and Society* 17 (January 1988): 6–8.

14. *Physics Today* 40 (June 1987): 45.

15. David Sanger, "Many Experts Doubt Star Wars Could be Effective by Mid-90's," *New York Times,* February 11, 1987, B1.

16. William Broad, "Star Wars Push Dimming Prospects for Exotic Arms," *New York Times,* March 9, 1987, A1.

17. Michael Gordon, "Nunn Seeks Shield for Missiles Fired in Error," *New York Times,* January 20, 1988, A1.

18. See Bruce et al., note 4.

19. "Brilliant Pebbles Missile Defense Concept Advocated by Livermore Scientist," *Aviation Week and Space Technology* 128 (June 13, 1988): 151–55. (Abridged version of Lowell Wood speech.)

20. Theresa Foley, "Sharp Rise in Brilliant Pebbles Interceptor Funding Accompanied by New Questions about Technical Feasibility," *Aviation Week and Space Technology* 130 (May 22, 1989): 20–21.

21. Charles Bennett, "Brilliant Pebbles? No, Loose Marbles," *New York Times,* June 17, 1989, L23.

8. Offensive Uses of Defensive Weapons

1. Matthew Bunn and Kosta Tsipis, "The Uncertainty of Pre-Emptive Nuclear Attack," *Scientific American* 249, (November 1983): 38.

2. Randall Forsberg, "A Bilateral Nuclear Weapons Freeze," *Scientific American* 247 (November 1982): 52–61.

3. McGeorge Bundy, "MX Not Buried Yet," *Bulletin of the Atomic Scientists* 39 (June–July 1983): 14–15.

4. "The Rail-Garrison MX and Midgetman Missiles," *Defense Monitor* 18, no. 5 (1989): 1–7.

5. *New York Times,* February 1, 1985, A3.

6. John Steinbruner, "Launch under Attack," *Scientific American* 250 (January 1984): 37–47.

7. Kosta Tsipis and Eric Raften, "Antisatellite Weapons: The Present Danger," *Technology Review* 87 (August-September 1984): 55–63.

8. John Pike, "Anti-Satellite Weapons," *Federation of American Scientists Public Interest Report* 36 (November 1983): 1–16; Richard Garwin, Kurt Gottfried, and Donald Hafner, "Antisatellite Weapons," *Scientific American* 250 (June 1984): 45–55.

9. Ashton Carter, "The Relationship of ASAT and BMD Systems," *Daedalus: Weapons in Space, Vol. I* 114 (Spring 1985): 171–89.

10. John Tirman and Peter Didishiem, "Lethal Paradox: The ASAT-SDI Link," in John Tirman, ed., *Empty Promise: The Growing Case Against Star Wars* (Boston: Beacon Press, 1986).

11. Office of Technology Assessment, *SDI: Technology, Survivability, and Software* (Washington, D.C.: Government Printing Office, 1988).

12. Colin Norman, "The Dark Side of SDI," *Science* 235 (February 27, 1987): 962–63.

9. Third-Generation Nuclear Weapons

1. *Congressional Record* 132, no. 108 (August 8, 1986): S10852–56.

2. Kosta Tsipis, "Third-Generation Nuclear Weapons," in *World Armaments and Disarmament: SIPRI Yearbook 1985* (London and Philadelphia: Taylor and Francis, 1985).

3. Warren Strobel, "SDI's Nuclear Shotgun on Pentagon's Fast Track," *Washington Times,* April 22, 1987, 1.

4. Theodore Taylor, "Third Generation Nuclear Weapons," *Scientific American* 256 (April 1987): 30–39; "Third Generation of Nukes," *Time,* May 25, 1987, 36.

5. See Taylor, "Nuclear Weapons," note 4; Theodore Taylor, "Endless Generations of Nuclear Weapons," *Bulletin of the Atomic Scientists* 42 (November 1986): 12–15.

10. Strategic Defense and Arms Control Treaties

1. Jozef Goldblat, *Agreements for Arms Control: A Critical Survey* (Cambridge, Mass.: Taylor and Francis, 1982).

2. Douglas E. Kneeland, "A Summary of Reagan's Positions on the Major Issues of This Year's Campaign," *New York Times,* July 16, 1980, 14.

3. Jeffrey Smith, "Star Wars and the ABM Treaty," *Science* 229 (July 5, 1985): 29–30.

4. John Fialka, "Reagan Team Justifies Star Wars Plan by Claiming Loophole in ABM Treaty," *Wall Street Journal,* October 22, 1985, 64; Charles Mohr, " 'Star Wars' Dispute," *New York Times,* October 17, 1985, A4.

5. "Excerpts from a Speech by Schultz at North Atlantic Assembly Meeting," *New York Times,* October 15, 1985, A6; John B. Rhinelander, "Reagan's 'Exotic' Interpretation of the ABM Treaty," *Arms Control Today* 15 (October, 1985): 3–6.

6. John B. Rhinelander and James P. Rubin, "Mission Accomplished: An Insider's Account of the ABM Treaty Negotiating Record," *Arms Control Today* 17 (September 1987): 3–14; Alan B. Sherr, "Sound Legal Reasoning or Policy Expedient? The 'New Interpretation' of the ABM Treaty," *International Security* 11 (Winter 1986–1987): 71–93.

7. "Six Former Defense Secretaries Support Traditional Interpretation of the ABM Treaty," *Arms Control Today* 17 (April 1987): 28.

8. Joseph R. Biden, Jr., and John B. Ritch III, "The End of the Sofaer Doctrine," *Arms Control Today* 18 (September 1988): 3–8.

9. Charles Mohr, "5 Former US Officials Urge Delay in 'Star Wars' Testing," *New York Times,* August 17, 1986, A1.

10. Michael Gordon, "New Tests Urged on Missile Shield," *New York Times,* May 10, 1987, A1.

11. Strategic Defense Initiative Organization, *1989 Report to the Congress on the Strategic Defense Initiative,* Appendix C, March 13, 1989.

12. Matthew Bunn, "ABM Treaty Compliance: Star Wars Tests on Shaky Ground," *Arms Control Today* 18 (April 1988): 11–19.

13. Theresa Foley, "SDI Moves into Test Era with New Systems," *Aviation Week and Space Technology* 129 (November 7, 1988): 36–37; Colin Norman, "SDI: Testing the Limits," *Science* 239 (January 15, 1988): 246–48.

14. "SDI Delta Star Satellite Readied for Targeting Research Flight," *Aviation Week and Space Technology* 130 (March 6, 1989): 32.

15. Theresa Foley, "US Prepares for First Test of Neutral Particle Beam in Space," *Aviation Week and Space Technology* 130 (May 15, 1989): 56–62.

16. John Pike, "Goals of the ABM Treaty," *Federation of American Scientist Public Interest Report* 40 (September 1987): 1–12.

17. David Dickson, "Proliferation Treaty Hinders SDI," *Science* 229 (July 12, 1985): 142.

11. The Strategic Defense Initiative and European Allies

1. Jonathan Dean, "Europe in the Shadow of Star Wars," in John Tirman, ed., *Empty Promise: The Growing Case Against Star Wars* (Cambridge, Mass.: Beacon Press, 1986).

2. "Europeans Link SDI Participation to Technology Transfer Issue," *Aviation Week and Space Technology*, 122 (February 18, 1985): 21.

3. "United States Technology Transfer Practices Will Guide Europeans to SDI," *Aviation Week and Space Technology* 122 (June 3, 1985): 125–33; "Barriers to European Participation in the Strategic Defense Initiative," report by John Pike to the Subcommittee on Economic Stabilization of the Committee on Banking, Finance, and Urban Affairs in House of Representatives (December 10, 1985).

4. "Britain Signs MOU to Participate in SDI," *Aviation Week and Space Technology* 123 (December 16, 1985): 12.

5. David Fairhall, "Britain Signs up for Star Wars," *Manchester Guardian,* December 7, 1985, 1.

6. Dave Dickson, "British Cabinet Split on SDI Agreement," *Science* 230 (December 13, 1985): 1251–52.

7. Phillip Boffey, William Broad, Leslie Gelb, Charles Mohr, and Holcomb Noble, *Claiming the Heavens* (New York: Times Books, 1988), chap. 8.

8. "Germans Insist on Technology Gains as Part of SDI Cooperation," *Aviation Week and Space Technology* 122 (April 8, 1985): 21.

9. James Markham, "Kohl in an Accord on Space Defense," *New York Times,* March 20, 1986, A6.

10. John Tagliabue, "Bonn is Criticized Over 'Star Wars,' " *New York Times,* April 5, 1986, A8.

11. See note 7.

12. Judith Miller, "Western Europeans, Some with Doubts, Support 'Star Wars,' " *New York Times,* December 30, 1985, A1.

13. David Dickson, "Europe Tries a Strategic Technology Initiative," *Science* 229 (July 12, 1985): 141–43; Ivo H. Daalder, *The SDI Challenge to Europe* (Cambridge, Mass.: Ballinger, 1987), chap. 4.

14. Clyde Haberman, "Japan Undecided about 'Star Wars,' " *New York Times,* February 10, 1986, A7.

15. "Japan Won't Guarantee 'Star Wars' Participation," *Des Moines Register,* September 10, 1986, A1.

16. See note 1; David Dickson, "A European Defense Initiative," *Science* 229 (September 20, 1985): 1243–45.

17. Dan Charles, "SDI Proponents Propose European End Run around the ABM Treaty," *Federation of American Scientists Public Interest Report* 39 (November, 1986): 10–12.

18. Ivo H. Daalder, "A Tactical Defense Initiative for Western Europe," *Bulletin of the Atomic Scientists* 43 (May 1987): 34–39.

19. Benoit Morel, "ATBM—a Solution in Search of a Problem," *Bulletin of the Atomic Scientists* 43 (May 1987): 39–41.

20. "United States Officials Reassure Thatcher Early SDI Deployment Not Planned," *Atlanta Journal,* February 26, 1987.

21. "INF Missile Treaty Wins Senate Approval," *1988 Congressional Quarterly Almanac XLIV* (Washington, D.C.: Congressional Quarterly News Service, 1989), 379–99.

12. Space Weapons in the Economy, Nuclear War, and Disarmament

1. Jeffrey Smith, "Pentagon's R&D Chief Roils the Waters," *Science* 232 (April 25, 1986): 443–45.

2. *Tailspin (The Korean Airline Disaster),* a 1988 HBO film.

3. Richard P. Turco, Owen B. Toon, Thomas P. Ackerman, James P. Pollack, and Carl Sagan, "The Climatic Effects of Nuclear War," *Scientific American* 251 (August 1984): 33–43; Richard P. Turco, Owen B. Toon, Thomas P. Ackerman, James P. Pollack, and Carl Sagan, "Nuclear Winter: Global Consequences of Multiple Nuclear Explosions," *Science* 222 (December 23, 1983): 1283–92; Carl Sagan, "Nuclear War and Climatic Catastrophe: Some Policy Implications," *Foreign Affairs* 62 (Winter 1983–1984): 257–92.

4. "A Treaty Limiting Antisatellite Weapons," in R. Garwin, Kurt Gottfried, and Henry Kendall, *The Fallacy of Star Wars* (New York: Vintage, 1984), Appendix 3; Richard Garwin, "ASAT Treaty Verification," chap. 15 in Kosta Tsipis, David W. Hafemeister, and Penny Janeway, *Arms Control Verification: The Technologies That Make It Possible* (Washington, D.C.: Pergamon-Brassey's, 1986).

5. Randall Forsberg, "A Bilateral Nuclear-Weapons Freeze," *Scientific American* 247 (1982): 52–61.

6. "The First Step: Halt Nuclear Weapons Testing," *Defense Monitor* 13, no. 1 (1989).

7. Lynn Sykes and Jack Evernden, "The Verification of a Comprehensive Nuclear Test Ban," *Scientific American* 247 (October 1982): 47–55; Kosta Tsipis, "Arms Control Pacts Can Be Verified," *Discover* 8 (April 1987): 79–93; Kosta Tsipis, David W. Hafemeister, and Penny Janeway, *Arms Control Verification: The Technologies That Make It Possible* (Washington, D.C.: Pergamon-Brassey's, 1986).

8. "Study Finds Treaty Compliance," *Bulletin of the Atomic Scientists* 43 (October 1987): 30–31.

9. Herbert York, "The Debate over the Hydrogen Bomb," *Scientific American* 233 (October 1975): 106–13.

Epilogue

1. Robert Bowman, *Star Wars* (Los Angeles and New York: Jeremy Tarcher/St. Martin's Press, 1986), Appendix F.

2. Robert Bowman, "Brilliant Pebbles and the New Star Wars Debate," *Space and Security News* 6 (April 1989), 3–10.

3. *Strategic Defense System: Stable Design and Adequate Testing Must Precede Decision to Deploy.* U.S. General Accounting Office Report to the National Security Subcommittee of the House of Representatives Committee on Government Operations (Washington, D.C.: GPO, July 1990).

4. "Space Warfare: A New Cold War Battleground," *Defense Monitor* 19 (1990); Charles A. Monfort, "ASATs: Star Wars on the Cheap," *Bulletin of the Atomic Scientists* 45 (April 1989): 10–13.

5. Frank von Hippel, "How to Avoid Accidental Nuclear War," *Bulletin of the Atomic Scientists* 46 (June 1990): 35–37.

Appendix 4. How the Chemical Laser Works

1. "Report to the American Physical Society of the Study Group on Science and Technology of Directed Energy Weapons," *Reviews of Modern Physics* 59 (July 1987): chap. 3.2.

Appendix 5. Number of Satellites Needed for a Chemical-Laser Defense

1. Richard Garwin, "How Many Orbiting Lasers for Boost-Phase Intercept?" *Nature* 315 (May 23, 1985): 286–90.

2. Hans Bethe and Richard Garwin, "Appendix A: New BMD Technologies," *Daedalus: Weapons in Space, Vol. II* 114 (Summer 1985): 339–46.

3. George Field and David Spergel, "Cost of Space-Based Laser Ballistic Missile Defense," *Science* 231 (March 21, 1986): 1387–93.

Appendix 6. How the X-ray Laser Works and the Laser Gain Achievable

1. F. Bunkin, V. Dershiev, and S. Yakovlenko, "Specification for Pumping X-ray Laser with Ionizing Radiation," *Soviet Journal of Quantum Electronics* 11 (July 1981): 971–72.

2. David M. Ritson, "A Weapon for the Twenty-First Century," *Nature* 328 (August 6, 1987): 487–90.

3. "Soft X-ray Laser at Lawrence Livermore Lab," *Science* 226 (November 16, 1984): 821–22.

4. "Experts Cast Doubt on X-ray Laser," *Science* 226 (1985): 821–22.

5. Ed Walbridge, "Angle Constraints for Nuclear Pumped X-ray Laser Weapons," *Nature* 310 (July 19, 1984): 180–82.

6. Kosta Tsipis, "Third Generation Nuclear Weapons," in *World Armaments and Disarmament: SIPRI Yearbook 1985* (Oxford: Oxford University Press, 1985), chap. 3.

7. See note 2.

Appendix 7. Rise Height and Fuel Required for an X-ray Laser Boost-Phase Defense

1. Hans Bethe and Richard Garwin, "Appendix A: New BMD Technologies," *Daedalus: Weapons in Space, Vol. II* 114 (Summer 1985): 346–55.

Appendix 8. How the Excimer Laser Works

1. "Report to the American Physical Society of the Study Group on Science and Technology of Directed Energy Weapons," *Reviews of Modern Physics* 59 (July 1987): chap. 3.3.

Appendix 9. How the Free-Electron Laser Works

1. "Report to the American Physical Society of the Study Group on Science and Technology of Directed Energy Weapons," *Reviews of Modern Physics* 59 (July 1987): chap. 3.4.

Appendix 10. Power Levels Needed for the Orbiting-Mirror Defense

1. Michael Callaham and Kosta Tsipis, "High Energy Laser Weapons: A Technical Assessment," Report No. 6 (Program in Science and Technology for National Security, Massachusetts Institute of Technology, 1980), sec. 3.

Appendix 11. Power Required for a Neutral-Beam Defense

1. "Report to the American Physical Society of the Study Group on Science and Technology of Directed Energy Weapons," *Reviews of Modern Physics* 59 (July 1987): chap. 4.

2. Ashton Carter, *Ballistic Missile Defense* (Washington, D.C.: Office of Technology Assessment, April 1984), sec. 3.4.

Appendix 12. Countermeasure of a High-Altitude Nuclear Blast

1. A. Boyles, "Nuclear Explosions," *American Journal of Physics* 50 (July 1982): 586–94.

Appendix 15. Requirements for Space-Based Interceptors in a Boost-Phase Defense

1. David Spergel and George Field, "What Price Space-based Interceptors?" *Nature* 333 (June 30, 1988): 813–15.

Appendix 23. Brilliant Pebble Boost-Phase Requirements

1. Gregory Canavan and Edward Teller, "Strategic Defense for the 1990s," *Nature* 344 (April 19, 1990): 699–704.

2. Richard L. Garwin, "Brilliant Pebbles Won't Do," *Nature* 346 (July 5, 1990): 21.

3. Myron Lecar, "Absentee Ratio for Boost-Phase ASATs," *Nature* 331 (February 11, 1988): 489.

Glossary

Ablative Coating: Material used to coat the surface of a missile or warhead that has a high heat capacitance and evaporates when heated, taking thermal energy with it.

Accidental Launch Protection System: Proposal introduced by Senator Sam Nunn to use technology developed under SDI to develop a terminal-site defense consistent with the ABM Treaty to protect against accidental nuclear launch.

Acquisition: Process of searching for and detecting a potential target for a strategic defense in a space environment.

Adaptive Optics: An optical system used to correct distortion in an optical beam. This can be used to correct certain atmospheric distortions in the laser beam of the mirror boost-phase defense.

Advanced Launch System: A sequel to the space shuttle capable of transporting heavy loads up to 200,000 pounds into space, which will be essential for deploying the first-phase SDI defense.

Airborne Optical Adjunct: The system being developed for long-wave infrared acquisition of warhead targets in the terminal-phase defense.

Airburst: A nuclear explosion in air above the surface of the Earth.

Anti–Ballistic Missile: A term from the 1960s for a missile built for the purpose of intercepting and destroying a strategic ballistic missile or the warheads it releases. Currently refers to any device to counter ballistic missiles.

Antisatellite Weapon: Weapon used for the purpose of destroying satellites, typically a satellite armed with explosives or a military plane armed with homing rockets.

Antitactical Ballistic Missile: A missile, generally ground-based, designed to counter shorter-range tactical missiles.

Architecture: Designed structure of a system (e.g., a defensive system) that shows the basing and interaction of the sensors, weapons, and battle-management computers.

Ballistic Missile: A missile following a trajectory set by the fuel-burning stages of the missile in its boost phase.

Battle Management: The process of managing military systems under battle conditions to assure coordination and achievement of objectives. For a strategic defense, this requires computer hardware and software to coordinate detection, tracking, targeting, kill assessment, retargeting, and defense against counterattacks by the offense.

Beta Blackout: Blackout to all frequencies lower than a critical frequency behind the plasma (ionized gas) cloud created by a nuclear explosion. The critical

241

frequency is determined by the density of free electrons (beta particles) in the plasma cloud, which varies with the time after the nuclear detonation.

Blast Wave: One effect produced by a nuclear explosion; the significant overpressure from the explosion travels out at faster than the speed of sound, creating a shock wave with the normal atmospheric background.

Booster: The missile with its fuel-burning stages that lifts the payload (warhead) from the launch site into a ballistic trajectory.

Boost Phase: The first phase of a launched ballistic missile, in which the fuel of the missile is burnt in one or more stages to boost the payload on a set path.

Boost-Phase Surveillance and Tracking System: A system under development for a strategic defense that surveys the area of a missile launch to detect the missiles (boosters) and tracks their path of motion (trajectory). This information would be passed on to the targeting systems.

Brilliant Pebbles: A concept for a boost-phase defense proposed in 1988 by Lowell Wood and Edward Teller of Lawrence Livermore National Laboratories in which small independent defense satellites (each a Brilliant Pebble) numbering in the tens of thousands would each protect a specific zone against ballistic missiles.

Bus (also known as Post-Boost Vehicle): The payload of a ballistic missile, containing the multiple independently targetable reentry vehicles (MIRVs, commonly referred to as warheads), guidance systems, propellants, and thrust devices for deploying each of the MIRVs and penetration aids.

Bus Deployment: The process of releasing each reentry vehicle (warhead) in the bus toward its designated target in the post-boost phase.

Chaff: Metal strips or metal foil released to reflect electromagnetic energy. For a strategic defense, this can be used as a countermeasure to reduce the destructive energy in lasers or to reduce effectiveness of detection and tracking of the targets.

Chemical Laser: A laser in which chemical reactions provide the pumping energy to produce the population inversion.

Counterforce: The targeting of accurate missiles and bombers to attack enemy weapons and military installations.

Countervalue: The targeting of missiles and bombers to attack population and industrial centers.

Cruise Missiles: U.S. accurate medium-range missiles that are not ballistic but follow a low-altitude path in the atmosphere powered by turbofans, with onboard computer capabilities for guiding them to their targets. They have a range of about 1,500 miles and can be launched from bombers and from the ground.

Directed-Energy Weapon: A laser or particle-beam weapon that directs destructive energy in a beam toward the target.

Eureka: A technology initiative for European countries started by France in 1985, probably as an alternative to the U.S. offers of technology development contracts under the Strategic Defense Initiative.

Exoatmospheric Reentry Vehicle Interceptor System: A homing missile designed for midcourse defense (outside the atmosphere) in the planned first-phase deployment of a strategic defense.

First-Phase Deployment: The plan for early deployment of a strategic defense using on the SBI, ERIS, and HEDI rockets to intercept the missiles, which has been the focus of the SDIO since 1987. This would be followed by later deployment stages utilizing laser and particle-beam weapons when they have been developed.

Fluence: Amount (e.g., of energy or power) per unit of cross-section (area) of a target.

High Endoatmospheric Defense Interceptor: A homing missile designed for terminal defense (inside the atmosphere) in the planned first-phase deployment of a strategic defense.

Hypervelocity Object: A small object accelerated to a high velocity in a railgun, designed to interact with the target to determine the location of the real warheads.

Imaging: The process of identifying specific objects in a background by obtaining high-quality images.

Intercontinental Ballistic Missile: A land-based ballistic missile with nuclear warheads and an intercontinental range capability, generally referring to missiles in the Soviet Union targeted on the United States or in the United States targeted on the Soviet Union.

Intermediate-Range Ballistic Missile: A ballistic missile with nuclear warheads and a range capability of around 1,700 to 3,500 miles.

Kill Assessment: Determination of the extent of damage to a target after it has been attacked.

Kinetic-Energy Weapon: A weapon that is used to damage or destroy a distant target by traveling to the target and colliding at high speeds or exploding at the site of the target.

Laddering: A terminal-phase scheme to hide warheads designated for a particular target from defense tracking. The warheads are preset to explode at a certain altitude, with warheads behind each group descending to successively lower altitudes and then exploding.

Medium-Range Ballistic Missile: A ballistic missile with nuclear warheads and a range capability of around 700 to 1,700 miles.

Midcourse Phase: The flight phase of a ballistic missile occurring after the warheads or reentry vehicles have been deployed from the missile payload, lasting until shortly after reentry into the atmosphere.

Multiple Independent Reentry Vehicles: The independent armed vehicles or warheads released from the payload of a missile, each of which can be independently targeted.

Neutral-Particle Beam: An energetic beam of neutral atoms created by accelerated ions up to high energies, then neutralizing them with electrons.

Peacekeeper: The innocuous name of the MX missile, a very accurate (counter force) American solid-fueled ICBM designed to be shuttled between silos in order to avoid destruction by a Soviet preemptive first strike.

Penetration Aids: Devices or methods on a missile or bus to counter defense attacks, such as camouflage, deception, or use of decoys.

Permissive Action Links: Coded switches on nuclear weapons which make enabling or disabling access to the nuclear warhead dependent on possession of the code.

Pershing: Medium-range U.S. ballistic missiles deployed in Europe. The Pershing Ia has a range of about 450 miles. The Pershing II missile has a capability for high accuracy and a range of about 1,000 miles. These are being removed under conditions of the INF Treaty.

Population Inversion: A condition for lasing in lasers in which a greater number of atoms or molecules in the laser are in the upper-energy state than in the lower-energy state. When these particles make a transition from the upper-energy state to the lower-energy state, they emit radiation, whereas a transition from the lower-energy state to the upper-energy state absorbs radiation.

Post-Boost (or Bus Deployment) Phase: The second phase of the ballistic missile after the fueled stages have boosted the missile to its final trajectory, in which the bus (payload) of the missile independently deploys each reentry vehicle (warhead) toward its target.

Prometheus: The SDIO project to develop the "nuclear shotgun," in which the blast wave from an underground nuclear explosion sends very high velocity pellets up a long cannon barrel to a target above the Earth's surface. This was a classified project first revealed publicly in 1987.

Pumping: The input of energy into a laser to maintain population inversion, allowing the laser to continue emitting a beam.

Railgun: A device for accelerating "bullets" (small objects, usually metallic) up to very high speeds, generally using electromagnetic forces.

Reentry Vehicle: Vehicle released from ballistic missile by the bus after the missile completes the boost phase, which carries a nuclear device toward a specific target zone.

Salvage Fusing: A countermeasure in the reentry phase where some warheads (reentry vehicles) are set to detonate when attacked. These explosions provide a shield to detection of warheads behind them.

Sensor: Electronic instrument to detect electromagnetic radiation or nuclear particle emission from distant objects, to aid in identifying and tracking targets.

Space-Based Surveillance and Tracking System: The strategic defense system under development that is designed for locating and tracking the reentry vehicles (warheads) in the midcourse phase.

Space Mines: Devices containing an explosive charge that can track and follow a target to destroy it upon command or attaining preset conditions.

Strategic Defense Initiative Organization: The branch of the Defense Department devoted to research, development, and eventual deployment of a strategic defense; the fourth branch of the armed services.

Submarine-Launched Ballistic Missile: A submarine sea-based ballistic missile with nuclear warheads; generally referring to missiles on Soviet submarines targeted on the United States or on U.S. submarines targeted on the Soviet Union.

Tactical Ballistic Missile: A short- or intermediate-range missile intended for use in war fighting after strategic missiles have been launched.

Terminal Imaging Radar: Radar systems for locating and tracking the reentry vehicles (warheads) in the terminal phase.

Terminal Phase: The short (lasting 2 minutes or less) final phase of a ballistic missile (beginning shortly before the reentry vehicles have reentered the atmosphere) in which the nuclear device on the vehicle or warhead is activated and exploded.

Third-Generation Nuclear Weapon: Nuclear weapons engineered for specific purposes, such as by concentrating part of the power of the nuclear explosion in a particular direction or enhancing certain aspects of the explosion.

Tracking: Monitoring the path (trajectory) of identified moving targets.

Trident II: A recent American SLBM of very high accuracy capable of carrying 10 to 15 warheads.

Warhead: A nuclear weapon device contained in the payload of a missile; commonly used to refer to a reentry vehicle.

INDEX